TRADE TASTE & TRANSFORMATION

TRADE TASTE & TRANSFORMATION
Jingdezhen Porcelain for Japan, 1620–1645

Julia B. Curtis

with contributions from
Stephen Little and Mary Ann Rogers

Edited by J. May Lee Barrett

China Institute Gallery
China Institute
New York
2006

Distributed by Art Media Resources, Ltd.

China Institute Gallery
Celebrating 40 Years of Excellence
1966 ~ 2006

This catalogue was published to accompany the exhibition
Trade Taste and Transformation: Jingdezhen Porcelain for Japan, 1620–1645
February 2–June 10, 2006

China Institute Gallery
125 East 65th Street
New York, NY 10021
212.744.8181

Library of Congress Control Number: 2005937726
ISBN-10: 0-9774054-0-0
ISBN-13: 978-0-9774054-0-4

General Editor and Project Director: Willow Weilan Hai Chang
Editor: J. May Lee Barrett
Designer: Peter Lukic
Printed in Hong Kong by Pressroom Printer and Designer

The *pinyin* system of romanization is used throughout the text and
bibliography except for the names of Chinese authors writing in Western
languages. Chinese terms cited in Western-language titles remain in their
original form and have not been converted.

China Institute was founded in 1926 by American philosopher John Dewey
and Chinese educator Hu Shih, together with other prominent educators.
It is the oldest bi-cultural and educational organization in the United States
with an exclusive focus on China and is dedicated to promoting the
understanding, appreciation, and enjoyment of Chinese civilization, culture,
heritage, and current affairs through classroom teaching and seminars, art
exhibitions, public programs, teacher education, lectures, and symposia.

Cover illustration (cat. no. 16)
Charcoal Container
Ming dynasty, ca. 1630–1645
Porcelain decorated in underglaze cobalt blue
H. 10.4 cm; W. 9.5 cm
Private Collection

Frontispiece (detail, cat. no. 9)
Dish
Ming dynasty, ca. 1625–1635
Porcelain decorated in underglaze cobalt blue
H. 6. 4 cm; W. 27.9 cm; D. 24.8 cm
Lent by the Asian Art Museum, Gift of Roy Leventritt (B69P98L)

This publication is dedicated to
my husband, John R. Curtis, for his constant encouragement,
his knowledge, and his judgement, which has influenced every aspect of this catalogue
and nourished our shared passion for Chinese art.

CONTENTS

SPONSORS OF THE EXHIBITION

*This exhibition and catalog have been made possible in part through the generous support of the following *

PATRONS
Blakemore Foundation
E. Rhodes and Leona B. Carpenter Foundation

LEADERS
John R. Curtis
Argie and Oscar Tang
Mary and James G. Wallach Foundation

CONTRIBUTORS
John S. Dyson
J.J. Lally & Co. Oriental Art

SUPPORTERS
Marie-Hélène and Guy A. Weill

INDIVIDUALS
Berwald Oriental Art
Michael E. and Winnie Feng
Hart and Nancy B. Fessenden
Agnes Gund and Daniel Shapiro
Margro R. Long
Robert W. and Virginia Riggs Lyons
Mechlin and Valery Moore
Theresa M. Reilly
Jeannette N. Rider
Linda Rosenfield Shulsky
Jeffrey Stamen
Robert P. and Barbara Youngman

We are also grateful for the continuing support to China Institute Gallery from
The Starr Foundation
China Institute's Friends of the Gallery

* At the time of printing

LENDERS TO THE EXHIBITION

Asian Art Museum of San Francisco

Butler Family Collection

Sir Michael Butler

Peggy and Richard M. Danziger

Private Collection

MESSAGE FROM THE BOARD OF TRUSTEES AND THE PRESIDENT OF CHINA INSTITUTE

This year China Institute celebrates its eightieth anniversary as a bi-cultural and educational organization dedicated to promoting the understanding, appreciation, and enjoyment of Chinese civilization and culture, past and present. It is also the fortieth anniversary of China Institute Gallery. Over the course of the past four decades, the Gallery has become an important and effective instrument of our educational mission. The exhibitions have not only been a visual feast of artistic and cultural treasures, but also a springboard for intellectual discussion and fresh ideas.

It gives us great pleasure to open this special year with the spring exhibition *Trade Taste and Transformation: Jingdezhen Porcelain for Japan, 1620–1645*, which presents a special moment in Chinese trade history. These export ceramics tell us more than we expect about two different cultures and leave us with a new level of appreciation for the role of commerce in the transformation of mundane objects. In the declining decades of the Ming dynasty, the Japanese market provided much needed revenue for the kilns at Jingdezhen. The Chinese potters filled the orders from Japan with blue-and-white (*kosometsuke*) and enamel-decorated (*ko'akae*) wares made as efficiently and cheaply as possible, often with technical imperfections not tolerated among their domestic patrons. But these imperfections suited the aesthetic taste of Japan's tea masters, and these wares, which were mainly used for the tea ceremony, are treasured to this day by Japanese collectors. We hope that this exhibition will not only stimulate American interest in this little-studied area of Chinese ceramics, but also that of the Chinese and Japanese audience. These unassuming wares have a quirky charm that can be appealing, and they deserve their spotlight on the art historical stage. On a broader level, these objects have much to say about the complex interrelationship of Chinese and Japanese culture.

We would like to thank the curator, Julia B. Curtis, for sharing with us the fruits of her research and to congratulate the Gallery Committee, the Gallery Director, Willow Weilan Hai Chang, and the gallery staff on a job well done. We are above all indebted to the Board of Trustees of China Institute, the devoted Friends of the Gallery, and The Starr Foundation for their continuing support. The project could not go forward without the additional support from the sponsors of the exhibition, for which we are extremely grateful.

Virginia A. Kamsky
Chair, Board of Trustees

Sara Judge McCalpin
President

FOREWORD

The renowned Japanese scholar and ceramics specialist Mikami Tsugio 三上次男 once said that the cultural exchange between the Eastern and Western worlds was recorded in Chinese ceramics. While tea was consumed and silk rotted, ancient Chinese ceramics shines on. Five decades ago, he introduced the phrase "The Ceramic Road" to describe the trade routes by which Chinese porcelain was transported to other Asian countries, Europe, and even Africa. The starting points of this route were mainly the ports along the southeastern coast of China; the three most renowned were Guangzhou (广州), in Guangdong province, Quanzhou (泉州), in Fujian province, and Mingzhou (明州), now known as Ningbo (宁波), in Zhejiang province.

An active relationship between China and Japan was recorded as early as the Tang dynasty. Between 630 and 894 CE, the Japanese government sent over thirteen delegations known as *kentoushi* (遣唐使), which was comprised of ambassadors, students, and monks, to the Tang capital at Chang'an (长安, present-day Xi'an 西安) to study Chinese culture. Remains of popular Tang ceramics, such as underglaze-painted Changsha Tongguan ware (长沙铜官窑), white-glazed Xing ware (邢窑), and green-glazed Yue ware (越窑), were also found at various archaeological sites in Japan, evidence that the ceramic trade between China and Japan was active at least in the seventh century.

Jingdezhen, in Jiangxi province, became the world's chief source of porcelain, especially blue-and-white ware. There were two major water routes for transporting porcelains from Jingdezhen to various ports. One route was westward along the Chang River (昌江 Changjiang) to Poyang Lake (鄱阳湖 Poyang hu), then south along the Gan (赣江 Ganjiang) and the Bei (北江 Beijiang) Rivers to reach the port of Guangzhou. The other route was along the Chang River to Poyang Lake, then north to Jiujiang (九江) to access the Yangzi River (长江 Changjiang) and reach ports, such as Ningbo (宁波), in the lower Yangzi. A major port during the Ming dynasty, Ningbo was designated by the government as the official loading point for porcelain bound for Japan and other Asian countries.

In the tumultuous period from 1620 to 1645, Jingdezhen potters welcomed the opportunity to create something different than what they were making for the European market. They created wares in a livelier, more intimate, and freer style to suit Japanese taste and to be used in the increasingly popular tea ceremony in Japan. Following the practice of the Ming period, the decorative patterns of *kosometsuke* and *ko'akae* ware made heavy use of rebuses and analogies to express traditional Chinese beliefs and values. For instance, the Three Friends of Winter 岁寒三友—bamboo, plum, and pine—which were notable for withstanding or blossoming in the cold of winter, express the Chinese concept of the ideal Confucian gentleman as one who shows courage, endurance, and integrity. And the wish for a prosperous family lasting many generations is represented through a depiction of melons and long tangles of vines, an image called *guadie mianmian* 瓜瓞绵绵. Such images, expressive of noble human qualities and desires for a happy life, were appreciated in both China and Japan. This exhibition thus provides us with vivid evidence of the commonality of human aspirations in different cultures.

These porcelains, made exclusively for export by Chinese potters, were not to be commonly found in the Chinese interior. Museum collections of export ware in China, therefore, were mainly dependent upon finds from recent archaeological excavations in the old port cities, at kiln sites, and at sites on the southeastern coast along trade routes, as well as upon salvage from shipwrecks found mainly in Guangdong and Fujian provinces. As a result of these finds, Guangdong is planning to build a museum of Chinese export porcelain. Still, the study of Chinese export porcelain is a fairly young discipline in China. It was only in the 1980s that the Chinese Export

Porcelain Research Association (Zhongguo Waixiaoci Xuehui 中国外销瓷学会) was established; the Association held annual symposia and published the papers. Later this organization was merged into the Chinese Ancient Ceramic Research Association (Zhongguo Gutaoci Xuehui 中国古陶瓷学会). In addition, scattered articles about export porcelains could be found in various journals. Even among these limited studies, very few touched upon the wares destined for Japan. Thus, this exhibition catalogue, with its focus on the dramatic period in which trade between Japan and China was encouraged, plays an important role in filling a void in this understudied area.

I would like to express my sincere gratitude to the various individuals and groups who made this exhibition and publication possible. Among those at the core of this project are the lenders to this exhibition, who have generously agreed to share their treasures with the public. The guest curator, Dr. Julia B. Curtis, had devoted years of study to these porcelains; she has worked arduously to select the objects in this exhibition and present us with a new understanding of the subject. In their contributions to the catalogue, Dr. Steven Little, Director of the Honolulu Academy of Art, and Mary Ann Rogers, a specialist on Chinese and Japanese art, shared with us their passionate appreciation of the aesthetics of kosometsuke and ko'akae ware. Their essays enhance our understanding of the broader historical and cultural context of these Chinese porcelains, so beloved in Japan.

This project could not have been successfully carried out without the support of the various foundations and individual sponsors of the exhibition, as well as the loyal Friends of the Gallery. The Trustees of the China Institute have been a source of continuing support and encouragement, while the Gallery Committee offered their expertise and guidance from the very inception of the project. Gallery staffers Jennifer Choiniere and Pao Yu Cheng worked diligently in handling the numerous tasks and details required to mount an exhibition and publish a catalogue. My sincere thanks also go to all the gallery docents, volunteers, and interns for their invaluable and selfless services. The entire China Institute staff deserves credit for their general support and enthusiasm for this project, but in particular I would like to thank Regina Rodwell-Bell and Matthew Marotta for their help in raising funds for this exhibition and Nancy Jervis and France Pepper for arranging the exhibition related symposium and lectures.

We are also fortunate to have a great team of independent specialists and professionals contributing their expertise to this project. J. May Lee Barrett did an excellent job editing the catalogue as well as the exhibition labels and all the didactic text; Perry Hu created a beautiful installation with his characteristic sensitivity to the aesthetics of the objects on display; Peter Lukic worked tirelessly under the pressure of our tight schedule to create an elegant design for the catalogue and other exhibition related graphics; Nicole Straus and Margery Newman organized the effort to bring this exhibition to the attention of the media and the public.

In addition, I would like to thank Mr. Zhang Pusheng, Professor Zhou Xiaolu, and Professor Jiang Zanchu for their assistance in creating the Chinese titles for the works of art in this catalogue and also for providing some important reference materials; Zhang Rongxiang for her translation of the Chinese summary and Linda Mao for typing the Chinese text. Special thanks go to Gregory Kinsey, a specialist in the Japanese tea ceremony; he not only provided many valuable insights and detailed explanations on how the porcelain objects in this exhibition were used for the tea ceremony, but also lent his lacquer trays for the exhibition. His performance of the formal tea ceremony, my very first, will always be a treasured experience. Finally, I would like to thank Sara Judge McCalpin, the new president of China Institute, for her understanding and support.

Willow Weilan Hai Chang
Director
China Institute Gallery

PREFACE

Notes to the Reader

This catalogue is only the third to appear in the past twenty-five years on porcelain made in Jingdezhen for the Japanese market between 1620 and 1645. It contains a wealth of information on Chinese iconography and rebuses and, to a lesser extent, Japanese symbolism. Much of Japanese iconography was received or adapted from China, so Chinese symbolism plays a major role in the decoration of these porcelains despite the significant Japanese influence on their production. I hope that the divisions of this catalogue will make this wealth accessible.

The first section of the catalogue includes wares whose shapes were determined by their roles in the Japanese tea ceremony, roles which may not be well known to the Western or Chinese reader. They are decorated with a wide variety of motifs which are explained in individual catalogue entries. The second section illustrates Japanese decorative conventions which were adopted by Jingdezhen potters to suit Japanese taste. In these two sections, readers can use the illustrations to guide their inquiries into the meaning of motifs and rebuses.

Chinese motifs and rebuses are the central focus of the last three sections of the catalogue. In section III, various types of floral and animal motifs are identified and their meanings indicated in the entries. Scholars' themes and motifs, presented in section IV, are important to most forms of Chinese art. They include landscapes and images of the scholar as specific historical figures and as generalized icon. Landscape in Chinese art serves the scholar as the locus for reclusion and self-cultivation. A brief explanation of the changing styles of landscape on porcelain can be found in the third essay and related catalogue entries. Finally, Daoist and Buddhist images and symbols were of great importance to spiritual life in China and Japan. Several of the most critical concepts of the two religions are briefly explained in section V as well as in the third essay and catalogue entry nos. 86 and 88 of section IV.

Kosometsuke and *ko'akae* wares are not well known in China or the West and have not been precisely dated even in Japan. So popular were these wares with tea enthusiasts that they were repeatedly copied in Japan beginning at least by the eighteenth century, and copies of *ko'akae* wares continued to be produced into the 1920s. Hence the need for detailed descriptions of potting characteristics, beyond the normal descriptions of Chinese porcelains usually contained in catalogue entries. The enumeration of these potting characteristics should enable students of Japanese-market wares to distinguish early porcelains from later copies (fakes). It should also help to establish chronologies for *kosometsuke* and *ko'akae* wares even within the twenty-five-year period covered by this catalogue. And the potting characteristics, particularly of *kosometsuke* ware, explain the spontaneity and naturalness of their production, which in turn explains much of their appeal to the tea people (Jp: *chajin*) of the 1620s through the 1640s. Finally, I hope the detailed descriptions of the *kosometsuke* wares in this catalogue will prove useful to Japanese archaeologists in their research into the role of these porcelains in seventeenth-century Japan.

Acknowledgements

This project has been a joint venture. Friends and colleagues have helped make possible this catalogue and the exhibition which accompanies it. I am particularly endebted to Alwine Crosby and Marian Arroyo, who make my work possible. My thanks also to Dr. Stephen

Little, Director of the Honolulu Academy of Arts, for his continuing enthusiasm for Jingdezhen porcelain made for the Japanese market between 1620 and 1645, as evidenced in his publications and his essay for this catalogue. Many years ago, Mary Ann Rogers dealt expertly with *kosometsuke* and *ko'akae* wares from the Idemitsu Collection in *In Pursuit of the Dragon*. Her continuing enthusiasm for these wares is evident in her essay for this catalogue, and she is among the very few Chinese ceramicists who knows Japanese stonewares of the late sixteenth and early seventeenth century as well. Terese Bartholomew, Curator of Himalayan Art and Chinese Decorative Art, has been generous with her precious time in providing me access over the years to the Effie B. Allison Collection and Roy C. Leventritt Collection in the Asian Art Museum of San Francisco. She supplied me with indispensable information, verbal and published, about botany and rebuses in Chinese art. I am particularly grateful for copies of her shorter publications, which are scarce and have been invaluable for this and other publications. Thanks also to Dr. Emily Sano, Director, Sharon Steckline, Registrar, and Dr. Michael Knight, Senior Curator of Chinese Art of the Asian Art Museum for the loan of objects in their care.

Thanks go to Louise Cort, Curator for Ceramics at the Freer-Sackler Galleries, for help with the bibliography on Japanese stoneware and an introduction to Meghan Jones, doctoral candidate at the Institute of Fine Arts, New York University, who aided me by translating texts from Japanese to English. My eternal gratitude goes to Professor Jonathan Chaves of George Washington University and to his colleague, Kikuchi Wakana, for translating Japanese texts heavily larded with Chinese characters into English. Professor Chaves also translated the poetic inscription in catalogue no. 48 and provided accompanying information in a timely manner. Also, my thanks go to Frauke Carlucci for translating the essay and catalogue entries of an exhibition on *kosometsuke* and *ko'akae* from German to English. I am indebted to Irene Finch in London, England, for supplying me with that particular publication.

The late Professor Oliver Impey helped train my eye early on when I was selecting porcelains from the Butler Family Collection for this exhibition. China Institute and I are again indebted to the Butler Family Collection for a large loan and to Sir Michael Butler for his time in arranging the photography of the wares. Peggy and Richard Danziger have been generous to loan their extraordinary porcelains to the exhibition. And Margot Paul Ernst provided me with guidance through the thicket of books in English on the tea ceremony and the use of vessel forms in the ceremony. She also supplied me with a rare volume on Japanese textiles by Amanda Stitchcombe, which Ms. Ernst played a role in producing.

I am grateful to numerous individuals at China Institute for their unstinting help, particularly Jennifer Choiniere, Registrar, and Willow Hai Chang, Gallery Director, as well as Pao Yu Cheng, the Gallery Assistant. Willow Hai Chang and J. May Lee Barrett are due special thanks for their help in better spelling out the rebuses in the catalogue entries and rendering them in more intelligible English. I owe an immense debt of gratitude to Mrs. Susan Canoy, who tirelessly and enthusiastically turned my handwritten pages into intelligible print and to J. May Lee Barrett, my superb editor, who corrected many infelicitous phrases, compiled the bibliography, and otherwise transformed a complex manuscript into readable form. Any errors therein are entirely my responsibility.

Julia B. Curtis

CHINESE SUMMARY 中文简介

贸易品味和嬗变：1620-1645年景德镇制外销日本的瓷器

景德镇外销瓷中最精彩的部分当属于1620-1645年间为出口日本而制作的瓷器。这些瓷器中包括日语名称中的"古染付"（"古青花"瓷）、"古赤绘"（"古色"瓷）和祥瑞。此次展览和图录是在日本国土以外首次将古染付和古赤绘中最广泛、最有代表性的瓷器荟集一堂。

本图录所体现的外销瓷的品味和变化发生在约1620-1645年间，其本身具有特别的原因。在此以前，万历皇帝统治的中国几乎濒临破产的边缘。十六世纪九十年代援助朝鲜抵抗日本以中国为最终目的的侵略战争和1619年中国东北部由努尔哈赤率领的强盛的满族部落对明朝的攻击，两场战争使得明代政权元气大伤。至1620年万历皇帝去世时，景德镇的陶瓷工业正处于艰难时刻，官窑已经被关闭。此前，陶工们已经为葡萄牙、西班牙、荷兰、土耳其、波斯和南亚制作瓷器达数十年之久，于是他们将目光转往日本以寻求新的市场。

制作技巧方面的不完善是古染付瓷所具有的特点，而这种欠缺正是日本茶道大师们所喜爱的。就其艺术精神面貌而言，古染付和古赤绘更类似玛丽·安·罗杰在其文章中所论及的伊贺窑水罐以及濑户、志野和美浓窑的日本瓷器。古染付瓷器中倍受推崇的特点之一是所谓的"虫食"效果。这一现象发生在由于陶土磨细不均匀时陶器本身收缩快于釉的收缩；当烧热的陶瓷冷却时，瓷器边缘和尖突部位的表面产生剥落现象。具有虫食效果的瓷器价格如此昂贵，以至日本的制陶者自十八世纪始便开始仿造这些瓷器。

古染付和古赤绘瓷器的装饰也与当时日本新的自然朴实的审美观有关。许多古染付瓷用最低劣的钴类色釉，烧成后呈蓝黑色。古染付瓷的装饰多以疾速的轮廓线条，飞舞的大笔触，不同色调的蓝色渲染为特点。天启年间（1621-1627）制作的古赤绘在钴蓝色的装饰上涂釉的手法也是非常的迅速。十六世纪三十年代和四十年代的古赤绘瓷的制作则比较讲究；瓷器需要烧两次而且釉必须仔细地涂在钴蓝色釉之上或瓷釉的轮廓线内。到十六世纪三十年代，景德镇的陶工们在为日本制作两种瓷器。一种是继续表现简朴和不规则的茶具风格特点，甚至在巧妙的点缀多色釉的瓷器上也是如此；而另一种则是迎合各种阶层品味的"通俗而有喜乐气氛"的带有装饰风味的瓷器，它与前者质朴的茶具风格形成鲜明对比。

此次图录和展览分为五个部分。第一部分包括专为日本市场制作的，在茶道中使用的器具。在为日本市场生产的所有瓷器中收藏价值最高的就是该部分的古染付瓷器。其中最大的瓷器是盛水罐，其作用是装新鲜水倒入铁壶中，然后烧成泡茶用的开水。第二大的容器为两个瓮，日本人称为水罐，字面的意思为"补充水的罐子"。另一件为茶道所制作的器具是一个小小的装香的容器，用来往有木炭的火盆里送香。该展览部分的其他器物的来源直接或间接地受到日本陶瓷器的影响，比如篮子形状的盘子（手钵），厚足底的盘子和食具。虽然历史学家们对这些商业贸易瓷器订单的流传过程所知甚少，最饶有趣味的、通常被认为是为茶道大师们而制作的器具，如形状特别的五件套、十件套或更多件套的碟子，其形状呈笛子或扇面，或动物，或蔬菜、花卉甚至人物形状，其令人惊叹的变化多端的形式反映了景德镇无名陶工们的创造性。

展览的第二部分表现的装饰具有独特的日本品味，它们也是帮助理解展览中大多数碟子和盘子上装饰图案的钥匙。这种装饰手法虽然与中国的审美品味格格不入，然而它们在日本的桃山时代（1573-1615）和江户时代（1615-1868）却非常流行。这些装饰手法包括器物图案设计的本身和图案各部安排的不对称性，使用分割块面或背景对比鲜明的方法以及片状（片身替，即唐織）的与纺织品设计有关的图案。

其他三个部分瓷器的图案设计深受中国题材和图像的影响，有些也是中国和日本文化中所共有的。其中的第三部分以自然万物为主题，这部分的专为日本制作的外销瓷常常布满动植物题材，这些器皿多是在茶道中使用的。第四部分全属中国题材，分别以特定或一般的文人士大夫的形象为图像。它们充分体现了文人士大夫在中国社会的显要地位，而这种地位是日本文人所不可等同的。该部分的瓷器也包括山水题材，往往和文人的隐居和修身养性有关。这些器物和图案表现了景德镇外销瓷在日本品味影响下所产生的风格变化。它们尺寸奇怪，背景歪斜，透视缺乏，形成了古染付瓷和古赤绘瓷的特点。

道教和佛教题材是古染付瓷和古赤绘瓷图像装饰的最后一个内容（展品第89—104号）。道教流传到日本的过程甚为复杂，到十七世纪初叶，使用这些瓷器的日本人应该对道教的八仙和道家的仪轨、人物和预言有所了解。佛教的题材也是非常流行，有些比较隐晦，如棕榈叶或竹筏正在离开现世的画面（展品第86、88号）。属于禅宗佛教圣徒内"非正规类别"的罗汉和其他人物的形象在古染付瓷和古赤绘瓷中也有表现。

图录中第一和第二部分为茶道仪式和日常生活所定做的瓷器，就直接反映出受到日本审美品味的影响。第三到第五部分的盘碟表现出景德镇的陶工们能够将传统的中国装饰题材改造成适用于他们所认为的日本品味中去。这种将各式图案题材运用于日用品上的尝试，体现了陶工们的灵活性和创造性，它使得古染付瓷和古赤绘瓷器在外销瓷中别具一格。最重要的是，古染付瓷和古赤绘瓷器揭示了景德镇陶工在技术上的全面性，并能按照需求灵活设计，这一切使得他们能创造出在其悠久的制瓷历史中最趣味横生、最变化多端和最亮丽显眼的为日本而制的外销瓷。

荣翔译自朱丽雅·柯蒂斯的英文简介

Chronology of Late Imperial China
and Corresponding Japanese Periods

China			Japan	
Song dynasty		960–1279	Heian period	794–1185
Northern Song	(960–1127)			
Southern Song	(1127–1279)		Kamakura and Nanbokucho period	1185–1392
Jin dynasty		1115–1234		
Yuan dynasty		1279–1368		
Ming dynasty		1368–1644		
Reign Eras				
Hongwu	(1368–1398)		Muromachi period	1392–1573
Jianwen	(1399–1402)			
Yongle	(1403–1424)			
Hongxi	(1425)			
Xuande	(1426–1435)			
Zhengtong	(1436–1449)			
Jingtai	(1450–1456)			
Tianshun	(1457–1464)			
Chenghua	(1465–1487)			
Hongzhi	(1488–1505)			
Zhengde	(1506–1521)			
Jiajing	(1522–1566)			
Longqing	(1567–1572)		Momoyama period	1573–1615
Wanli	(1573–1620)		Edo period	1615–1868
Taichang	(1620)			
Tianqi	(1621–1627)			
Chongzhen	(1628–1644)			
Qing dynasty		1644–1911		

LOCATION MAP OF JINGDEZHEN AND PORT CITIES OF CHINA AND JAPAN

THE VISUAL POETRY OF *KOSOMETSUKE* AND SHONZUI WARES

Stephen Little

The *kosometsuke* and Shonzui wares made by Chinese potters for the Japanese market in the final decades of the Ming dynasty (1368–1644) are among the most inspired, delightful, and unusual creations in the entire history of Chinese ceramics. Violating as they do many of the basic canons of taste and proportion that characterize the production of blue-and-white porcelains in China, they manifest an extraordinary burst of idiosyncratic creativity at a time of overwhelming chaos in Chinese social, political, economic, and military history.

My first encounter with *kosometsuke* and Shonzui wares came in 1977, when as an intern at the Asian Art Museum of San Francisco (the Avery Brundage Collection), I encountered the remarkable exhibition entitled Chinese Ceramics from Japanese Collections, organized by Seizo Hayashiya and Henry Trubner.[1] I will never forget being given the opportunity by the museum's director, René-Yvon Lefebvre d'Argencé, and curators Clarence Shangraw and Terese Tse Bartholomew to help install this exceptional show. The exhibition included several spectacular examples of *kosometsuke* ware, including a great *mizusashi* (water container for use in the Japanese tea ceremony) from a private collection, and a famous hexagonal dish with loop handles, depicting a scene from an early Japanese narrative such as *The Tale of Genji*, from the Tokyo National Museum.[2] Both vessels were made during the reign of the Tianqi emperor (1621–27). The *mizusashi* is similar to one in the current China Institute exhibition (cat. no. 3) and consists of a covered blue-and-white porcelain vessel in the shape of a wooden water bucket. Handling this vessel was a magical experience, and I particularly remember the beautiful silvery blue color of its underglaze cobalt oxide pigment, its roughly levigated clay, the slight bits of sand that adhered to the base within the foot ring, and most amazingly, the rough, cracked edges with the many *mushikui*

("insect nibbles")—the little chips in the glaze along the vessel's joins and edges. Having been taught to expect the more technically perfect features of most Chinese blue-and-white porcelains made from the Yuan (1260–1368) and Ming dynasties, I was astonished to discover a blue-and-white ware that not only incorporated such imperfections as extensive *mushikui*, but one in which these very features were considered—through the prism of seventeenth-century Japanese aesthetics and taste—the highest marks of authenticity and refinement.

In the same exhibition were also several wonderful examples of Shonzui ware, the more carefully constructed though no less whimsical and unusual blue-and-white ware made at the Jingdezhen kilns for export to Japan during the tortured final reign of the Ming, the Chongzhen period (1628–1644). This ware is named after the Japanese reading of a mysterious name (Ch: Xiangrui; Jp: Shonzui) that appears among the Chinese inscriptions on a number of surviving examples in Japanese collections.[3] One example I encountered in the 1977 exhibition was an elegant vase in the shape of a double gourd, also from the collection of the Tokyo National Museum, beautifully painted and incorporating the brown-glazed (iron-oxide) rim and a small roundel containing the image of a scholar riding a donkey that are so often found on Shonzui wares.[4] I remember bring struck by the remarkably bold and unusual design of this vase, so utterly different from anything I had ever seen before among Chinese ceramics.

The experience of handling these vessels and learning of the extraordinary degree to which they and others like them had been prized for over three hundred years in Japan made an indelible impression on me. It was with great delight that I discovered that the Asian Art Museum of San Francisco—the very museum in which I had just started working—owned a large collection of such wares (especially *kosometsuke* wares), thanks to the generosity of such donors as Effie B. Allison and Roy C. Leventritt. Many of the finest examples of these ceramics are included in the current exhibition. I spent many hours over the next several years in the basement storeroom of the museum, studying these and other Chinese porcelains of the

---

Opposite page (detail of cat. no. 41)
Dish
Ming dynasty, ca. 1635–1645
Porcelain decorated in underglaze cobalt blue and iron red
H. 2.5 cm; Diam. 14.5 cm
Private Collection

Transitional Period (1620–1683). This was a period in the late '70s and early '80s, when museum curators were still able to spend much of their time researching art—a period when blockbuster exhibitions were in their infancy, and the words development and fundraising were practically unknown. I was fortunate to be encouraged in my study of Chinese late Ming ceramics made for the Japanese market by my colleagues Lefebvre d'Argencé and Shangraw, both of whom were internationally recognized specialists in the history of Asian ceramics.

One thing I quickly discovered was the extent to which *kosometsuke* and Shonzui wares were largely unknown, or certainly poorly recognized and understood, by the majority of scholars and collectors of Chinese ceramics outside of Japan. In all fairness, this situation was beginning to change, thanks to such exhibitions as the 1977 Asia Society show and Richard Kilburn's landmark "Transitional Wares and their Forerunners," organized by the Oriental Ceramics Society of Hong Kong in 1981. I remember, for example, visiting the National Palace Museum in Taipei, Taiwan, in the summer of 1981 and being granted an audience with Chiang Fu-tsung, the venerable and esteemed director of that great institution. He asked me what kind of research I was doing, and I answered that I was studying the paintings of the sixteenth-century Wu School artist Qiu Ying and making a special study of *kosometsuke* and Shonzui wares (of which there were none in the collections of the National Palace Museum, the source of which were the former imperial collections of the Qing dynasty emperors in the Forbidden City in Beijing). When I discussed my great interest in and enthusiasm for *kosometsuke* wares, with their strange, whimsical, and asymmetric shapes and spontaneously painted designs, and mentioned that these wares were made in China for export to Japan during the Tianqi reign of the late Ming, Chiang merely looked at me and said, "Don't waste your time—these wares were all made in Japan!" Needless to say, at that point I changed the subject to Chinese painting, of which the National Palace Museum has the world's greatest collection. I realized that since *kosometsuke* and Shonzui wares were made in the early seventeenth century specifically for export to Japan, and since the vast majority of surviving examples are still in Japan today, many traditional scholars like Chiang had never seen such wares in Chinese collections.

The degree to which *kosometsuke* wares were valued in Japan was made clear to me when I began traveling in Japan and studying Japanese museum and private collections of Chinese art in the 1980s. I recognized that these wares had been prized for centuries as *densei-hin*, "handed-down objects" or heirlooms. I began to appreciate not only the traditional Japanese veneration for these rare and strange Chinese ceramics, but the old wooden boxes in which they were usually stored, often complete with paper documents inscribed by generations of earlier connoisseurs of the tea ceremony and its ceramics.

The special place in the history of Japanese culture and collecting for *kosometsuke* and Shonzui wares was made even clearer when I organized the exhibition "Chinese Ceramics of the Transitional Period" for the China Institute in New York in 1983.[5] As I began searching American museum and private collections for works to include in this exhibition, I remember being shown a Japanese copy or forgery of a Chinese *kosometsuke* vessel in the collection of the Los Angeles County Museum of Art. I have always been fascinated by such works, and have learned a great deal from paying close attention to the technical details of their manufacture. The vessel in question was a Japanese copy of a "Takasago" blue-and-white porcelain *kosometsuke* vase, an example of which is included in this exhibition (cat. no. 19). What struck me the most was the extent to which the maker of the nineteenth-century Japanese copy had carefully simulated the *mushikui* chips in areas where the glaze was thin. Imitation is the greatest form of flattery, and Japanese potters of the late Edo and Meiji (1868–1912) were skilled at creating copies and facsimiles of Chinese *kosometsuke* and Shonzui wares, to the extent that modern collectors need to be vigilant when examining such wares today.

One of the most striking aspects of *kosometsuke* wares is the way in which they so palpably bring to life the strange and difficult experiences of potters at Jingdezhen in the 1620s. Due to the death of the Wanli emperor in 1620 and the subsequent cessation of the vast imperial orders for blue-and-white porcelains, potters at the Jingdezhen kilns in Jiangxi province were suddenly without a major source of their patronage. It was fortunate, therefore, that two foreign sources of patronage were already on the scene at that moment—the Dutch and the Japanese. The Dutch had only recently maneuvered the Portuguese out of the position of primary control of the lucrative Chinese porcelain trade to Europe, and were desperate to fulfill the enormous demands for porcelain in the West (where the technique of manufacturing porcelain was still unknown and would remain unknown until the early eighteenth century). While the Japanese had been importing Chinese ceramics for centuries, it was only with the breakdown of the Chinese economy and traditional patterns of patronage in the 1620s that they were able, for the first time, to custom-order Chinese porcelains made in Japanese shapes; occasionally these vessels are also decorated with scenes from Japanese literature. This can only have been a momentous turn of events for both the Chinese potters at Jingdezhen and their Japanese clients, among whom were newly emerging *chajin* (tea masters, literally "tea people") of the early Edo period (1615–1867). These events coincided with the increasing popularity of the tea ceremony in Japan—particularly from the Momoyama (1568–1615) period onward—and the growing popularity of the aesthetic, such as is often seen among Japanese Mino and Oribe wares, of consciously rough, asymmetrical, and bold designs in both shape and decoration. The profusion of shapes among *kosometsuke* wares that were specifically made for use in the tea ceremony (bowls, fresh water containers, charcoal containers, trays and dishes for use in the *kaiseki* meal service, incense containers and burners, and flower vases) points to the growth and popularity of the tea ceremony within Japanese culture in the early seventeenth century, a time that also coincided with growing interest in objects of exotic (non-Japanese) manufacture—which by at least the mid-seventeenth century would include ceramics from Thailand and Holland among the prized wares used in the tea ceremony.

Of particular interest among both *kosometsuke* and Shonzui wares, but especially the former, is the marked presence of both melancholy and humor in their painted designs. The strangely contorted landscapes so often seen on *kosometsuke* wares and the frequently encountered Buddhist and Daoist scenes that can be both amusing and bizarre have long been taken in Japan as signs of the impending decline of the social fabric that characterized the final decades of the Ming dynasty. The early and mid-seventeenth century witnessed the near-complete breakdown of social order in many parts of China, with consequent disruptions in the economy and the political realm. The seeds for the eventual triumph of the Manchus, who invaded China and established the Qing dynasty in 1644, were sowed decades earlier, starting late in the reign of the weak and pathetic Wanli emperor (1573–1620). Both Daoist and Zen Buddhist themes proliferated on Chinese ceramics from the 1620s through the end of the Ming, and these proved popular in both China and Japan. Ironically, what characterized this time of social and political breakdown was an astonishing burst of creativity in the visual arts, attested not only in ceramics but in Chinese painting and other decorative arts as well. The degree to which this period witnessed a renaissance in freedom of expression in ceramic design, unimpeded by oversight from the imperial palace (a situation that obtained until the 1680s, well into the early Qing dynasty), was never again duplicated until the twentieth century. With the re-imposition of imperial control at the Jingdezhen kilns in 1683, early in the reign of the Kangxi emperor (1662–1722), Chinese ceramic production and design entered a new phase of consummate technical skill and polish, and tremendous experimentation in glaze technology, but with none of the freedom and whimsy on the part of individual potters that characterized the last turbulent decades of the Ming dynasty.

Today the *kosometsuke* wares of the 1620s and the Shonzui wares of the 1630s and early '40s are increasingly recognized as among the most unusual and creative manifestations of genius and artistic freedom in the history of Chinese ceramics. This exhibition brings the astonishing talents of both the Chinese potters and their Japanese patrons and clients of the early seventeenth century into a greater light than they have previously enjoyed in the West. As manifestations of enormous creativity in times of hardship, these ceramics survive as unique symbols of human strength and endurance.

NOTES

1. Seizo Hayashiya and Henry Trubner, et al., *Chinese Ceramics from Japanese Collections*, exhibition catalogue (New York: The Asia Society, 1977).
2. Ibid., nos. 64, 67.
3. For a discussion of these inscriptions, see Soame Jenyns, "The Chinese Ko-sometsuke and Shonzui Wares," *Transactions of the Oriental Ceramic Society*, 1962–63, 34 (1964): 13–50.
4. Hayashiya and Trubner, no. 72.
5. Stephen Little, *Chinese Ceramics of the Transitional Period, 1620–1683*, exhibition catalogue (New York: China Institute, 1983).

Overleaf (detail of fig. 1, p. 7)
Kosometsuke two-handled basin
China, early 17th century.
Idemitsu Museum of Arts, Tokyo
Photo courtesy of the Idemitsu Museum of Arts

踏馬執玉鞭平来上青勿評登

姮豚愛少年

"THE WILD BUNCH"—CHINESE PORCELAIN EXPATRIATES IN SEVENTEENTH-CENTURY JAPAN

Mary Ann Rogers

My first confrontation with tea-ceremony *kosometsuke* (which occurred in Japan at the same time as my first brush with indigenous Japanese ceramic styles) proved to be a rude and brutal assault on my senses. An education in London at the Percival David Foundation had not prepared me for anything but the most refined of ceramic styles, the most perfect of wares. With such Chinese ceramics as imperial blue-and-white porcelains as my heroic standard, I was not prepared for these outlaws called *kosometsuke*, this group of miscreants that were such obvious misfits within the gracious world of later Chinese ceramics. How *could* Chinese ceramic artists be so audacious? How was it possible for Chinese craftsmen of the late Ming period to diverge so defiantly from the well-beaten and familiar path forged by their predecessors over the many centuries leading up to the flourishing of *kosometsuke* during the early seventeenth century? The wares were indeed non-conformists, willfully unpredictable within a creative cultural milieu that treasured, banked on, and extolled conformity, leading me to understand and appreciate more fully the core qualities of *proper* Chinese ceramics simply by being so different.

I then found myself asking how *did* this lawless band, or what I came to call "The Wild Bunch" in reference to one of my husband's favorite movies, ever come into existence in the law-abiding world of Chinese ceramic styles? Taking the approach of a Chinese painting specialist, I considered the possibility that *kosometsuke* ceramics might be understood and accepted if they were considered creative transformations within a tradition, offsprings of that process by which great art was created and defined in China. But it became apparent on further examination and reflection that *kosometsuke* did not well up from within the creative genius simmering in the soul of a Chinese artist nor did it ever enjoy the acclaim in China that it would have garnered if such were the case. Although the media—the porcelain body and the cobalt pigment used for painting—were within the tradition of Chinese art, the message conveyed, that is, the style of these ceramics, was not. A rogue gene, as it were, had somehow entered the family of Chinese ceramics, changing the genetic code and rendering its message comprehensible only to outsiders, the Japanese, who had their own aesthetic reality and their own family values; it is only through their reality and their values that *kosometsuke* can be understood and appreciated today. Hence, the Chinese ceramic historian is compelled to cross deep waters in search of further enlightenment.

If we were able to visit early seventeenth-century Japan, where *kosometsuke* flourished, we would find a complex and fascinating sub-world existing within the larger Japanese social and cultural order. The aesthetic of this sub-world was born to a large extent from a desire and need to house the activities and paraphernalia surrounding the enjoyment and appreciation of a simple beverage: tea. A physical and spiritual environment with distinct customs and ethics, aesthetic codes, and inventories of furnishings and accouterments—these comprised the world of tea that had been evolving since the beverage was first introduced to Japan from China many centuries before. As a medicinal drink, as a stimulant in Buddhist monastic practices, and as a costly and rare elixir to bolster the social status of those able to afford it, tea eventually entered the ken of and came to be enjoyed by a broad spectrum of Japanese society, and it acquired in the course of time great social, educational, cultural, spiritual, and even political significance. The agenda was determined on the whole by savants of tea (*chajin*, "tea people"), along with the powerful political masters they served and advised, and the merchants involved in the production and traffic of tea and its accouterments. Each of these individuals had the potential to give his own spin to this world of tea, which dominated the cultural galaxy of the Japanese over many centuries.

The small number of individuals who were key to the evolution of this tradition produced at various junctures what would appear to the outsider to be serious internal contradictions within the code that regulated the world of tea, and these anomalies are important to an understanding of *kosometsuke*. The fact that a style of tea drinking that elevated poverty, spareness, humility, and naturalness to the highest stature could co-exist with a style that applauded refinement, opulence, affluence, and ostentation is in itself intriguing, especially when the two could

5

be promoted and articulated by a single master, as in the case of the tea master Sen no Rikyū (1522–1591) at the end of the 16th century. His world of tea could be housed in a tiny, humble thatch-roofed chamber which through its own utter simplicity and starkness showcases and enhances, one by one, each object used in the service and prompts the appreciation of each sound (water dripping into a pool) and fragrance (the incense, the grasses, the tea itself), or it could expand into a most splendid and lavish gathering where tea and food were consumed in large quantities by great numbers of guests or participants using a vast quantity of tea and dining implements.

Contradictions within a stylistic, or actually philosophic, lineage of tea drinking were also present. For example, the values of simplicity and rusticity, which were held paramount in one important style of tea-drinking, encouraged the identification and use of objects or vessels characterized by naturalness, unpretentiousness, and honesty. A simple, hefty agrarian water jar with irregularities and roughnesses, cracks and blisters, and smudges and smears resulting from firing in a rude open kiln could serve excellently to store tea leaves and even grace the proceedings of a tea gathering with its withered, astringent beauty. On the other hand, it was also possible to use objects crafted very purposefully to make them look natural and unpretentious, and possible moreover to encourage and even direct their fabrication, a conceit that would seem to be the height of artificiality and pretentiousness. A vase could be fabricated from a thick piece of clay manicured to look like an ancient branch and slashed with a potter's knife or spatula to simulate a natural crevice, with perhaps a smattering of ash fired to look like moss, or a bowl might have its mouth rim pushed and pulled into an irregular shape and its side forcibly caved in—deformities that were not accidental or accidents of nature but purposeful, done to achieve a particular effect. It was in both the abstract and the physical worlds, in conceptual and visual features alike, that these contradictions existed. Yet the very ability to embrace or, better, to conjoin the contradictory and the mutually exclusive was one of the most remarkable features of the tea tradition in Japan, one that provided this world with the potential to remain rich and vital throughout the centuries. The immense aesthetic elasticity and flexibility of this tradition allowed for antithetical forces not only to coexist but to do so in complete harmony and synchronicity.

The development of this unique aesthetic balancing act in Japan was catalyzed not only by the artistic, aesthetic, and philosophical concerns of certain *chajin* but also by the political and economic realities of the world they lived in. China had long been the primary source for cultural paraphernalia within the world of tea. Whether a particular program was marked by the sanctity and reserve of a monastic ritual or by the ostentation and flamboyance of a secular festival, Chinese wares dominated. Although the intimate association of Chinese wares with tea consumption in Japan was to continue, the absolute centrality of Chinese wares disappeared when collections of Chinese art and utensils and the wealth that supported them were dispersed or totally lost during the civil warfare between 1467 and 1477. Necessity then demanded that less costly and more easily available native Japanese wares be used in the world of tea; home-produced and homely wares came swiftly to be appreciated for their humility, their plebian roughness, and their complete lack of pretension. Elevated to the ranks of desirable objects by tea cognoscenti, suitable pieces were consciously sought out and many types were "discovered" for use in the sophisticated activity known as the tea ceremony.

This shift in collecting focus as well as the new aesthetic bent resulted in a reassessment in Japan of what was held desirable from China. Such commonplace Chinese wares as the later Longquan celadons came to be accepted despite their drab yellowish glazes, the imperfection of their glaze crackles, or even an unsightly mend. When a broken Song period Longquan celadon bowl of the twelfth to thirteenth century, perfectly shaped and covered with a seductive cool green glaze of the highest quality, was returned to China for replacement on behalf of its owner, the eighth Ashikaga shogun Yoshimasu (1435–1490), it was returned with an unsightly repair, rough metal clamps holding the pieces together. Rather than taking offense that a new bowl had not materialized nor allowing disappointment that the Chinese no longer produced such exquisite wares to rule the day, the returned bowl gained new and greater stature because of the aesthetic tension between the elegant perfection of the ceramic and the simple strength of the repair itself. The spindly shapes and dark color of the clamps suggested a gathering of locusts on the green surface. Hence, the bowl was christened Bakō-han, "Locust Clamp." Bestowing such evocative names upon ceramics is one measure of the importance of individuality, of uniqueness, of "personality" that ceramics carried in the minds of the Japanese.

One can easily imagine the monk and *chajin* Murata Jukō (1422–1502) holding up the Bakō-han Longquan bowl and capturing the attention of Yoshimasu with this novel and surprising appreciation of the disfigured voy-

踉蹌跛少年
踏馬執玉鞭平安上青勿評登

Fig. 1. Kosometsuke two-handled basin. China, early 17th century. Idemitsu Museum of Arts, Tokyo. Photo courtesy of the Idemitsu Museum of Arts

ager upon its return to Japan. Jukō is indeed credited with opening the hearts of Yoshimasu and their compatriots to a deep spiritual component in the appreciation of tea and opening their eyes to the values of simplicity and humility, thus making possible the appreciation and use of lesser quality wares from China. The later, inferior celadons imported from China are known even today in Japan as "Juko *seiji*" (Jukō celadon). Even more important was the elevation, prompted by Jukō, of humble Japanese wares to the realm of tea, not an easy climb after the long history of the almost exclusive use of Chinese wares. The first step was the use of agrarian jars for tea storage, a usage of which Louise Cort has noted: "Only a tea man already deeply experienced in the use of Chinese ceramics in the traditional manner was ready to dissolve the boundaries between native and foreign by adding the Japanese jars to his assemblage of utensils."[1] From a Chinese perspective, Jukō indeed effected a creative transformation of tradition and paved the way for his successors, beginning with his most immediate disciple Takeno Jō-ō (1502–1555), to delight in the discovery of objects for tea ceremony use and eventually to engage in a very conscious and sophisticated manipulation of native wares into tea-ceremony utensils. The promotion of wares from Iga, Bizen, and other local potteries and the directing of these wares towards a specific aesthetic,

including deformation, asymmetry, and sculptural dynamism, encouraged what was originally rough and natural to move further along that aesthetic path until ceramics which had existed quietly on the sidelines, oblivious to their own roughness, their cracked and crawling glazes, their globs of glassy accretions, began to speak a new visual language. The way was paved for a tea world populated by native Shigaraki, Bizen, Iga, Seto, Raku, Shino, and Oribe wares and for a world that could also easily welcome and incorporate, along the way, new wares from China, culminating in the wave of *kosometsuke* made expressly for the Japanese tea aesthetes in the early seventeenth century.

Underglaze-blue-decorated wares produced outside of the imperial center at Jingdezhen became noteworthy to the Japanese for the same reasons they were dismissed by any informed Chinese, that is, for their imperfections and irregularities, substandard glazes and colors, and the swiftly executed and seemingly careless designs. Such ceramics were embraced in Japan because they appeared natural and unaffected, modest and unassuming, spontaneous and instinctive. *Minyao*, "people's ceramics" or "folk ware," thus was of greater significance to Japanese artistic and cultural life than merely a manageable stylistic springboard to help launch the Japanese porcelain industry. These wares occupy one extreme in the *kosometsuke* spectrum as defined by the Japanese. In a way similar to the adoption of plebian, home-made wares into the world of tea, these "folk wares" from China were thought of as "found" or "discovered." And, as in the case of an agrarian jar that had little aesthetic worth in its place of origin—that is, down on the farm—but was elevated in stature by tea men in metropolitan centers, so too were the plebian blue-and-white wares from China elevated to new and, from a Chinese point of view, unimaginable and unmerited heights. Not only did the Japanese world of tea accept these outsiders that were resolutely ignored in their homeland, but this world also influenced a new generation of *kosometsuke*, through the example of their own native up-to-date tea wares, on how to look and act.

Of a large two-handled *kosometsuke* basin (fig. 1) owned by the Idemitsu Museum of Arts in Tokyo, I wrote some years ago: "The walls are thick, the piece heavy and the shape distorted. The unglazed recessed base was raggedly scraped out, leaving a coarse surface that has burned a rusty brown. Kiln grit adheres to the vestigial foot. The relatively bright, bluish-tinged glaze is uneven, pitted and cracked, and dotted with dark iron spots. The glaze has separated and peeled extensively from the mouth rim and handle edges."[2] However it might look to the Chinese art specialist, these features are not to be considered flaws; this is the way the ceramic was intended to look, and if any of the features described above occurred spontaneously, all the better. One can also men-

Fig. 2. Shino water container named Kogan (Weathered Shore). Japan, early 17th century. Hatakeyama Memorial Museum of Fine Art, Tokyo. Photo courtesy of the Hatakeyama Memorial Museum of Fine Art

tion the great tactile quality of the piece, a characteristic no Chinese ceramic historian expects to confront in any post-Song period ceramic. While Chinese ceramic precedents hardly prepare us for appreciating such physical peculiarities, certain ceramics born and bred in Japan do, particularly the Shino wares produced in Gifu prefecture, formerly Mino province (fig. 2).

Shino was not a "discovered" ceramic, produced for other purposes only to be adopted or adapted as a tea ware. Sixteenth-century undecorated white-glazed tea bowls similar in shape to standard Chinese *temmoku* and Japanese Seto *temmoku* precedents appear to have developed rapidly into what much later came to be known as Shino. The raw materials of the Mino region resulted quite naturally in the production of extremely thick, opaque feldspathic glazes which imparted such a tactile quality to the ceramics that they are far closer in effect to the native Raku wares despite the difference in color than to anything from China, save perhaps the Jian tea bowls of yore which were also appreciated for their tactile qualities. Shino originated during the later sixteenth, or possibly the early seventeenth century, in order to fill the aesthetic bill of the times with thickly potted vessels that were rough, irregular, or skewed; that were covered in thick white glazes whose muted surfaces were pocked with holes, rented with cracks, and sometimes scarred with burns from the fire of the kiln; and that were decorated with subdued, suggestive, restrained, and intriguing underglaze painted designs. The most distinguished and prized *kosometsuke* exhibit a close kinship to such Shino wares in their physical demeanor: thick ceramic walls and "untrue" shapes, undulating sides and rims, and the so-called *mushikui* (literally, "insect-nibbled") mouths. They are, in fact, to a great degree understandable only in light of this Japanese ceramic star.

This kinship, however, does not fully account for the *kosometsuke* style of decoration. Shino and *kosometsuke*, when each is considered at full bloom, are quite distinct from one another even though decorated Shino did receive its initial impetus from imported Chinese-made wares, specifically the "folk" blue-and-white ware from Fujian province. Regardless of the pigment used—the easily accessible and common iron ores or the much rarer cobalt—the effect of underglaze painting on Shino is stunningly different from that on the vast majority of Chinese underglaze-painted wares, including wares from regional or provincial kilns. The thick feldspathic Shino glazes naturally and dramatically affected the appearance of the underglaze designs, sometimes giving the impression that

Fig. 3. Clog-shaped black Oribe tea bowl. Japan, early 17th century. Peggy and Richard M. Danziger Collection. Photo courtesy of Peggy and Richard M. Danziger

they are trapped in the thick glazes, dwelling below the surface. The glazes diffuse the thickly brushed-on pigments, creating a suggestive atmospheric quality; as the pigments forced their way to the surface, they appear to have heaped and piled themselves into such images as mountains or trees. In contrast, the underglaze paintings on Chinese stonewares and porcelains are normally viewed through thin clear glazes, and the colors, whether iron brown or black or cobalt blue, are clear and distinct and the motifs or pictures lucid and legible. In this respect *kosometsuke* did not depart from its Chinese roots.

In contrast to the calm and contemplative aspects of the Shino aesthetic, seventeenth-century *kosometsuke* can be dynamic and flamboyant, jaunty and witty, and thus a kindred spirit of Oribe ware, another product of the Mino kilns and a ceramic intimately associated with Shino but at the same time possessing a personality all its own (fig. 3). Furuta Oribe (1544–1615), the Momoyama period *chajin* who advised and influenced the most powerful military and political figures of his day, was born into the military class, and this association had a great influence on his aesthetic orientation. He began as a student of Sen no Rikyū but eschewed the spiritual aspects of Rikyū's taste in favor of a style of tea that would appeal to the military class, a style that was at once dramatic, ornate, and secular and noted for a sense of independence and individualism, for its bravura and life-affirming nature. Oribe is credited with a creative flare that sparked the innova-

tive styles of Mino ceramics: Black Seto and Yellow Seto, Shino as described above, the powerful Black Oribe tea bowls, and the dashing polychromatic Oribe wares (fig. 4), which are his real namesakes. If *kosometsuke* shares the body and soul of Shino, then it can be said to share the face and spirit of Oribe ware.

Furata Oribe left the imprint of his taste on the appearance of both ceramic form and ceramic decoration. In regard to form, his penchant for asymmetrical and irregular shapes, combined with an admiration for the broken or the damaged piece, extended to a delight in blatant, purposeful distortions without which certain *kosometsuke* creations are unimaginable. As far as actual vessel shapes are concerned, a line-up of *kosometsuke* examples could easily be formed consisting of only those based on Japanese wares or even specifically on those produced in Mino. But whereas the Mino potters specialized in abstract forms—for example, the plethora of small geometrically shaped serving dishes for the *kaiseki* meal—*kosometsuke* dishes were created in the forms of real fruits, flowers, vegetables, and leaves; of fish, birds, and mammals; and of such objects as shells or musical instruments. In this respect *kosometsuke* did not stray from its roots and remained grounded in the here and now, in the "real" human-centered world in which abstraction has little relevance.

Mino tea-ware decorators had at their fingertips a vast garden of motifs from which they were encouraged

9

to reap, generously sharing the harvest with the makers of *kosometsuke*. Motifs include uncomplicated and basic fare such as squares, circles or stripes, triangles, and various other geometric or diaper patterns. *Kosometsuke* decorators followed the Mino lead with such motifs as isolated bridges, a swath of fishing nets, or a waterwheel, images used not so much to suggest a wider world beyond the borders of the picture but rather to literally zoom in on the subject and to focus on its isolation, on that single moment of perception, and on the calm oasis that one can find within the wider world. Many subjects, drawn from a shared lexicon of plant and animal life and from the realm of streams and mountains without end, appear in both wares, but the Japanese decorators are more likely to schematize a subject or image and apply it to the ware in such a manner that its design values exceed its representational ones.

Motifs which appear in the Japanese and *kosometsuke* wares alike include floating cherry blossoms. Individual flowers, presumably drifting through the air from branches above, are usually silhouetted against a blank ground while a few wavy lines might indicate the stream or pond upon which they bob and float; blossoms painted on the inside of a water jar would appear to be floating in actual water when the vessel was filled. The subject of cherry blossoms has a Song-dynasty (960–1279) ceramic precedent in the decoration of *temmoku* wares from China, where the decor was appreciated because of its simple, unaffected beauty and the deep poetic reverberations of the image. The name *temmoku* was bestowed upon the dark-glazed tea bowls from China's southern provinces by the Japanese, who had collected the wares over many centuries; the term is the Japanese pronunciation of Tianmu, the name of a mountain where communities of Chan monks in monasteries welcomed their brethren from Japan, instructed them in religious matters, and exposed them to the fine arts as well as such necessities as ceramic bowls for drinking tea. The most significant of the wares known as *temmoku* were the tea bowls made at the Jian kilns in Fujian and the Jizhou kilns in Jiangxi province. Whereas these were designed for tea-drinking in China and were appreciated even by Song-period emperors, no one appears to have had such a long-standing devotion to these warmly comforting and decoratively subdued, sultry vessels nor to have collected the type and used it more avidly over subsequent centuries as the Japanese. Throughout tea history in Japan, the use and possession of a Chinese *temmoku* tea bowl was of great significance. It is not surprising then that the

temmoku and celadons of the Song and early Yuan (12th–early 14th c.) had such an extraordinary impact on the development of Japanese ceramics. The Chinese-inspired wares of the Seto kilns flourished from the Kamakura (1185–1333) through the Muromachi (1392–1573) periods, and the Seto kilns in turn provided the foundation and springboard for the wares of Mino; the intimate association of Seto and Mino production and tradition is suggested by the term *setomono*, coined for wares which would eventually be known as Shino and Oribe many decades after they originated.

We may take note here of another Chinese ware which is known by its Japanese name and is collected and used primarily in Japan: *kinrande* (gold-brocade design), the mid to late Ming overglaze-enameled porcelain embellished with gold. While these vividly colored and richly ornamental ceramics answered to the taste of Japan's sixteenth- and early seventeenth-century shogun and *daimyo*, *kinrande*, with its shapes and designs that did not depart far from the Chinese norm, was still essentially and foremost a Chinese ware that was tweaked and embellished, and sent to market. It was not until the production of *kosometsuke*, however, that a ware was made in quantity in China for the exclusive use of a single foreign client, in this case of course the Japanese, which is some measure of how powerful foreign consumers of Chinese goods became during the late Ming and the pressing economic necessity for the Chinese to respond to foreign taste. Of course Japan was not the only customer on the minds of the potters; the home market, western Asia, and Europe also had their ceramic needs and requirements.

Another subject which appears in the wares of Mino and in *kosometsuke*, the fruiting grapevine, is known particularly from Song-dynasty paintings associated with Chan aesthetics (and from paintings produced in the Japanese world of Zen after the Chinese prototypes). The decoration was in fact originally inspired by contact with the West. Grape cultivation was introduced to China from Western Asia during the Six Dynasties period (220–589), and the motif commonly appears in the arts of the Tang dynasty (618–906) and thereafter as an exotic addition to the world of Chinese design. It was an inherently rich subject with interestingly shaped, complex leaves that vary in size, plump fruits growing in massed bunches, delicate tendrils that stretch, curve and curl, sturdy trunks that could appear rough and withered by contrast, and the possibility of a fence, gate, or trellis to support the bountiful vine. The grapevine became a popular textile design in Japan, where cloth of

Fig. 4. Oribe dish with handle. Japan, early 17th century. Suntory Museum of Art, Tokyo. Photo courtesy of the Suntory Museum of Art

the most staggering beauty was produced during the Momoyama period (1573–1615) by craftsmen whose creations were crucial to Furuta Oribe's creative life. A method of decorating material called *tsujigahana* resulted in designs (not entirely dissimilar to those on the *kinrande* wares mentioned above) characterized by solidly-colored portions of fabric adjacent to undyed areas which were embellished with brush-painted and sometimes stitched decoration. The technique, originating in the manufacture of plebian fabric and clothing, was elevated during the Momoyama period to stunning heights for use in high society, a corollary to the elevation of lower class ceramics to the ranks of the elite.

The startling juxtapositions, the contrast of bold and bright or darkly somber color fields with fluid, sometimes exquisitely delineated pattern, is breathtaking, and the idea was used to brilliant effect in the decoration of green-glazed Oribe wares (fig. 4). Patterns associated with *tsujigahana*—linked polygons such as hexagons that look like tree bark or tortoise shell—appear not only in Oribe but in Shino wares as well, as do lozenges or diaper patterns, crosshatched fences and fishing nets, grasses or reeds, waterwheels, boats, bridges, small dwellings, umbrellas and fans, a lone bird or small flock, detached leaves and blossoms as well as flowering plants, plum, pine, willow, and bamboo, and more. Arrangements of small dots used in the designs of both Shino and Oribe are likely based on effects created by a tie-dying technique known as *shibori*, in which numerous tiny bunches of fabric are tied independently, holding them in reserve from the dye. Whereas viewing numbers of small *kosometsuke* dishes from China is like browsing through an album of late Ming paintings leaf by leaf, viewing such Oribe and Shino ceramics is like thumbing through swatch upon swatch of gorgeous fabrics.

Explicitly "Japanese" subjects found in *kosometsuke* but absent from Shino and Oribe include ceramic dishes in the shape of Mount Fuji or caricature-like painted images of tigers similar to those depicted in Japanese and Korean paintings and widely collected in Japan. Another intriguing subject is that of Japanese scholars and officials, recognizable by their garb and headgear and Japanese-style wagons or carts. Such subjects were known to the Chinese through drawings and perhaps documents recording the peculiarities of those who dwelled beyond the borders of the Middle Kingdom, as well as through actual contact with foreigners. In an eleventh-century copy of a scroll painting of the type known as "Tribute Bearers," thought to have been executed in 539, foreign emissaries line up to pay obeisance to the Chinese ruler, seeking political recognition and economic benefits through the gifts and messages they bear.[3] Among the many exotic foreigners portrayed in this painting, only the envoy from Japan is shown without shoes. Many centuries later during the late Ming period, if the images on *kosometsuke* wares are accurate, that style had not gone out of fashion, since the Japanese are shown unshod there as well (fig. 5).

In order to produce for the Japanese market, the Chinese kilns had to have been provided instructions, presumably by merchants from Japan as well as Chinese merchants visiting clients in Japan, in the form of wooden or paper templates for shapes and drawings or even paintings to illustrate the desired subjects and compositions. The Korean ceramic shapes favored in Japan and reproduced by *kosometsuke* potters, for example deep bowls with exaggerated mouth rim clefts and notched foot rings, would have been known to the Chinese potters also by way of Japanese emissaries. However, we might assume that once an aesthetic was understood, or once the potters and decorators "got the idea," they advanced on their own, producing creative variations that would please, and perhaps amuse, their customers. For example, certain subjects unusual in any ceramic context—gatherings of parasols or hats, or herds of oxen or horses—were treated by *kosometsuke* deco-

rators as if the motifs were stamps or stickers to be distributed in either haphazard or preconceived arrangements over the surfaces of the ceramics, whether they be bowls, dishes, or ewers. The images appear to float in thin milky air, conveying the playful worlds and the dreamlike moods valued by the Japanese.

Knowledge of the arts and fashions in China, including the ways and means of the artist, architectural and scientific precepts, and literary and theatrical arts among other things, were conveniently available to the Japanese through the circulation of illustrated woodblock-printed books, which proliferated especially in late Ming China. These provided models and inspiration and were an important source for later Japanese painters. A school of Japanese painting known as Nanga (which emulated styles associated with the literati or "Southern School" of painting in China) owed a good measure of its bold, stiff brushwork, its schematic renderings of rocks, mountains, trees, and water, and its lack of nuance or atmosphere to the fact that the Japanese artists were learning and copying from woodblock prints rather than actual paintings. These same styles and approaches are not unknown in the landscape subjects of Japanese ceramic decorators, especially in the Shino wares discussed here. On the other hand, the *kosometsuke* decorators were quite well equipped to deal with landscape depictions in their own terms. With quick and glib motions of the brush—scribbling a mountain range in cobalt, smoothing on the pigment to form a low plain or hillock, dotting and jabbing to indicate a tree or some shrubbery—the Chinese decorators created landscapes on ceramics that were equally suitable for the home market, for the West, or for the Japanese.

Very rarely were human figures used by Japanese decorators of tea-ceremony ceramics to achieve the abstract, the poetic, or the impressionistic effects that are the hallmarks of their wares. In *kosometsuke* it is quite the reverse. Human figures on *kosometsuke* range from images of jubilant children to gentlemen enjoying afternoon walks, conversations, or scholarly pastimes, to fishermen in their skiffs, to ladies harvesting mulberry leaves, all drawn from the common pool of Chinese decorative motives used on ceramics regardless of their intended destination—whether households in the vicinity of the kilns, the palace in Beijing, or beyond. This does not mean that poetic or romantic images were not possible. In fact, one of the most evocative examples is the above-mentioned Idemitsu basin, where the solitary figure on a donkey traverses a world of white porcelain and pauses on his jour-

Fig. 5. *Kosometsuke* hot-charcoal container. China, early 17th century. After Kawahara Masahiko, *Ko-sometsuke*, vol. 1, *Color Section* (Kyoto: Kyoto Shoin, 1977), p. 141, cat. nos. 111, 112

ney to view a poem floating in the sky overhead. In other less successful examples of this subject, where the figure is not focusing on the written words, the connection is not made and the composition then seems a pastiche. Similarly, a perfectly evocative image may be destroyed by the presence of humans. For example, the effect of a close-up view of a bridge section is destroyed when small figures are introduced, changing the scale and the entire

meaning of the image; this was an addition that some Chinese decorators apparently found irresistible.

The appearance in *kosometsuke* decoration of eccentric Daoist adepts and Buddhist monks, subjects with longstanding roles in the worlds of Chan, or Zen, art, is not surprising given the great contemporary relevance of seeking spiritual escape from the social, political, and economic turbulence of late Ming China. Lohan

13

(Sanskrit: *arhat*; Jp: *rakan*; Ch: *luohan*), disciples of the Buddha, attracted the attention of a number of artists who diverged from orthodoxy in their attitudes and in their art. Their interest was not in portraying remote monastic realms of reclusion and quietude but rather in presenting a rambunctious world of eccentric characters, strange in mien, sometimes deformed in physique, accompanied by beasts real or imagined, and quirky in posture as they tended to their chores and their conjurings. These depictions provided an escape from the tensions of the late Ming secular world into a spiritual cosmos with its own harmless brand of insanity. A scene of numerous lohan scattered across a landscape on a *kosometsuke* plate or dish has a similar visual effect as that of the densely populated world of as many as five-hundred disciples created by such painters of the late Ming as Wu Bin (1568–1626) and Ding Yunpeng (ca. 1575–1638). The Buddha's disciples along with other well known figures from Buddhist and Daoist lore are often portrayed individually on small *kosometsuke* dishes, and it is not at all difficult to find their counterparts in contemporaneous painting.

A particularly inventive portrayal of a lohan by a Chinese ceramic artist occurs on an elongated type of quatrefoil dish: the center is occupied by a single lohan painted in underglaze blue and surrounded by a vast kaleidoscopic quilt-work ground in colorful overglaze enamels, likely meant to convey the appearance of a monk's patchwork robe and possessing stunning decorative quality in its ceramic context. The abstract concept and surprising juxtaposition are in fact quite unusual and more akin to what one might expect from a Japanese artist. However, at the time when this type of dish was produced the colored glaze in Oribe wares was limited to a bright leaf green and Japanese overglaze-enameled porcelains had yet to be invented. In Japan such multi-colored Chinese porcelains are often referred to as *Tenkei-aka-e*, "red-decorated (wares) of the Tianqi (era)." These polychromatic porcelains are aesthetically related to *kosometsuke* wares, whose primary period of production is believed to have been during the Tianqi reign era (1621–1627) and soon thereafter, and were of course intended for the same market. They do not often stray in decorative scheme or subject matter from their Chinese foundation. But when the enamels are applied to forms appropriate to the Japanese tea ceremony and with geometric designs prompted by the Japanese aesthetic, the results are especially delightful and very modern in feeling.

A gentleman seated languorously on a pier with fishing pole in hand under outlandishly large lotus and swaying leaves is the primary decoration on a number of particularly engaging *kosometsuke* dishes. The figure likely represents the Song period philosopher, Zhou Dunyi, known for his love of the lotus flower. He could easily have drifted out of a painting by the late Ming artist Chen Hongshou (1598–1652), who in fact called himself Laolian, "Old Lotus." Known for his unconventional and eccentric renderings of human figures, Chen was among a number of painters who embarked on paths of great individualism by expressively distorting images, creating unnaturally elongated faces, wildly contorted mountain peaks, impossibly perforated rocks, or gargantuan flowers. Landscape was the subject most easily susceptible to the various inventive convolutions and distortions created by Chinese painters, and the results were shockingly abusive to the orthodox tradition, just as porcelain distortions in the hands of *kosometsuke* potters were an affront to the orthodox ceramic tradition. The deformed shapes of *kosometsuke* ceramics, then, not only had relevance to the Japanese market for which they were intended, but they also situated the Chinese potters smack within a contemporaneous artistic movement in China. The ceramics produced by *kosometsuke* artists are today intriguing in part because of their freedom from conventional constraints, and they might even be construed as emblems of their time. This should not, however, obscure a more basic and immediate reality: although they might have been among the Japanese tea master's prized possessions and might have exhibited their star power at gatherings of the rich and famous, *kosometsuke* were most important at the time of their production as a means to stave off economic catastrophe for many of the potters at Jingdezhen.

If Jukō, Rikyū, and Oribe made the *kosometsuke* style possible, then their successor, Kobori Enshū (1579–1647), the early Edo-period tea savant supreme after Oribe's death, made it the economic success that it became. Although the style and character of tea-ceremony *kosometsuke* were beholden to and intimately associated with the products of the Mino kilns, its appears to have been made after the death of Oribe. Thus, it was during Enshū's watch, as supported by tea-ceremony diaries of the time, that such *kosometsuke* poured into Japan. It has been said that "Enshū's tea possessed neither the spiritual strength of Rikyū's nor the intense creative quality of Oribe's. It was, rather, a style of tea broad enough to admit many standards, richly varied according to the requirements of time and place and constantly striving to make the most of all the tea utensils of both old and contemporary times."[4] Enshū's taste was indeed extremely catholic in its wide acceptance of various historical contributions of the tea world, absorbing novelties from the West and newly discovered implements from neighbors closer to home, allowing for the world of tea to be enriched by this potpourri of elements that caught his attention or were commissioned by him. Enshū's aesthetic embraced both rusticity and refinement, each with their deep historical moorings, and in their fusion—in "rustic elegance" or "elegant rusticity"—his aesthetic acquired great contemporary relevance. Whereas Jukō had set the stage with his removal of any barrier between what was Japanese and what was foreign, Enshū directed perfectly up-to-date performances on that stage. And further, as stated by Cort, "If Oribe took essential qualities of old wares and sculpted them into dramatic exaggeration, Enshū detached those characteristics from the rustic originals and superimposed them on thin, sleek urban objects, as a sort of a *wabi* grace note."[5] *Kosometsuke* then was designed for success. Built into it were the aesthetic requirements of Rikyū, of Oribe, and of Kobori Enshū.

Having been born in quick and effective response to the aesthetic communicated in the wares of the Mino kilns, *kosometsuke* also had within itself the potential to be more, to be something different again; *kosometsuke* in turn gave birth to a style known again exclusively by a Japanese name, Shonzui. The irregular, awkward shapes of *kosometsuke* were transformed into forms that were elegantly asymmetrical, producing a "new" ware imbued with an up-to-date finesse that Enshū would have been the first to appreciate. Just as the Oribe and other tea-ceremony wares of Enshū's time came under his very watchful eye, with shapes, colors, and glaze effects even sometimes specifically prescribed by him, the creation of Shonzui was completely controlled. The glazes of Shonzui are bright, even, and smooth; the underglaze blue is applied in studied ornamental designs that are perfect in concept and execution, while the bases and feet are evenly cut and trimmed and a smooth brown wash seals the mouth rims of the vessels. The concern in Shonzui for technical finish, for achieving predictability and perfection, brought Chinese wares made for the Japanese market back into the Chinese fold, theoretically at least. While the Chinese were, and in fact continue to be, oblivious to both Shonzui and *kosometsuke*, both wares have since the seventeenth century continued to work their special magic on the Japanese, a magic that now reaches out to an even wider world.

NOTES

1. Louise Allison Cort, *Shigaraki: Potters' Valley* (Tokyo, New York, and San Francisco: Kodansha International Ltd., 1979), p. 104.

2. Mary Ann Rogers, in *In Pursuit of the Dragon: Traditions and Transitions in Ming Ceramics, an exhibition from the Idemitsu Museum of Arts*, ed. Suzanne Kotz (Seattle, Wash.: Seattle Art Museum, 1988), p. 148.

3. The painting is in the Nanjing Museum. For references to illustrations, see James Cahill, *An Index of Early Chinese Painters and Paintings* (Berkeley, Los Angeles, and London: University of California Press, 1980), p. 52.

4. T. Hayashiya, M. Nakamura, and S. Hayashiya, *Japanese Arts and the Tea Ceremony*, adapted and translated by Joseph P. Macadam (New York: Weatherhill, 1974), p. 118.

5. Cort, *Shigaraki*, p. 171.

Overleaf (detail, cat. no. 47)
Dish
Ming dynasty, ca. 1635–1645
Porcelain decorated in polychrome enamels
H. 3.4 cm; Diam. 15 cm
Butler Family Collection

Trade Taste and Transformation: Porcelains from China to Japan, 1620–1645

Julia B. Curtis

The most fascinating export wares ever produced in Jingdezhen were made for the Japanese between 1620 and 1645. These include wares referred to in Japanese as *kosometsuke* ("old blue and white"), *ko'akae* ("old colored"), and Shonzui. This exhibition and catalogue examines the most extensive and representative group of *kosometsuke* and *ko'akae* wares ever assembled outside Japan. The foresight of two earlier collectors, Effie B. Allison and Roy C. Leventritt, whose collections are now at the Asian Art Museum of San Francisco, and the focused efforts of Sir Michael Butler, Richard Kilburn, and Georg Weishaupt in the 1970s and 1980s have made it possible to handle and study these wares, which are so highly treasured that they are seldom seen outside Japan.[1] A few other collectors in the West, including Peggy and Richard Danziger, have acquired examples of the best *kosometsuke* wares and shared them with the public. Shonzui wares are not included in the exhibition because they are not available to borrow in the West. As Masahiko Kawahara has remarked, "there are hardly any opportunities to admire [Shonzui wares] outside Japan."[2] These wares (fig. 1) resemble the fine Chinese domestic porcelains made in 1630s and 1640s. Formed from highly levigated clays, Shonzui wares have white bodies and glazes and are painted with a refined cobalt which sometimes fires a brilliant violet blue. They are intensely decorated with much fine brushwork and are light years away in feeling from the later sixteenth- and early seventeenth-century Japanese stonewares, particularly Shino and Oribe wares, which influenced the potting and decoration of *kosometsuke*, at least in spirit.

Detailed descriptions of the porcelains in the catalogue entries make it very clear that the Japanese had a good deal of influence on these wares. This conclusion follows logically from the fact that many of the forms and some of the decoration on *kosometsuke* and *ko'akae* wares were new to Jingdezhen in the 1620s. Close cultural ties between China and Japan undoubtedly facilitated the transmission of Japanese demand for new forms and decoration; the Japanese were steeped in Buddhism and Daoism and had a long tradition of appreciating Chinese art, artifacts, and literature. These ties are reflected in motifs that are shared but sometimes interpreted differently by the two cultures.

The wide variety of new shapes that the Jingdezhen potters created for use in the Japanese tea ceremony are a source of delight. Moreover, the potters' attempts to

Fig. 1. Shonzui bowl, ca. 1630–1645. Exterior and interior views. Porcelain decorated in underglaze cobalt blue, h. 7 cm, diam. 12 cm
Ex coll.: Richard Kilburn

cater to Japanese taste extended beyond shapes to all facets of decoration on even the simplest bowls and dishes. The use of asymmetry, in the design itself (as in cat. no. 37) and in the placement of decorative elements on the vessel (as in cat. no. 33), was done to appeal to the Japanese but would have been anathema to the Chinese. Jingdezhen potters adopted the heavy use of diaper patterns like those found on Japanese textiles and even copied an actual textile design in their attempts to meet Japanese market demands (see cat. no. 43). These remarkable adaptations, extreme examples of trade taste, make up the first two sections in this catalogue. The last three sections illustrate the transformation of Chinese themes interpreted for the Japanese market and a few purely Japanese themes as well.

The lack of artifice which characterizes *kosometsuke* wares was particularly appealing to Japanese tea masters. In that spirit, *kosometsuke* and *ko'akae* resemble Japanese stonewares: Iga water jars and the Seto, Shino, and Oribe wares discussed in Mary Ann Roger's essay. But Iga water jars and Oribe and Seto wares were often warped by hand, not just in the kiln; Iga jars often had ash thrown on them to roughen the surface and give the effect of quick, spontaneous, and carefree production, so as not to appear slick and hard-edged like the earlier Chinese ceramics treasured by the Japanese. By the 1620s, however, the potters of Jingdezhen managed to achieve the same effortless effect simply by following their own time-honored methods for producing bottom-of-the-line porcelains.

By the late Wanli period, around 1600 to 1619, the clay used in Jingdezhen for much export porcelain was poorly levigated; the good quality clay of the Ma Tang hills had been exhausted. It takes a considerable investment of time to purify, or levigate, poor quality clay. So for cheaper domestic wares and such export wares as *kraak* and *kosometsuke* porcelains, the potters did not take the time to bring the clay up to the standard of earlier Ming reigns. This poorly levigated clay sometimes resulted in chunks of grit popping through the glaze on the front as well as the backs of these wares and in some cases even caused bubbles in the glaze. At the very least, the small particles caused pinholes to pierce through the glaze, a fault very prevalent on *kosometsuke* and *ko'akae* wares. The poorly levigated clay also warped naturally in the kiln. This defect is particularly noticeable in square dishes (although in one case [cat. no. 90] it was probably encouraged by the potters) and in larger dishes and baskets formed from thick slabs of clay. But even small wheel-thrown bowls warped naturally during firing. A blue-and-white dish decorated with

a deer, monkey, bird, and wasp (cat. no. 55) and the water jar decorated with lion dogs (cat. no. 4) are dramatically warped. This imperfection testifies to the spontaneity with which *kosometsuke* and some *ko'akae* were potted, a spirit which endeared them to seventeenth-century tea aficionados in Japan.

One of the most highly valued characteristics of *kosometsuke* wares are the *mushikui*, "moth-eaten edges," which occurs when the badly levigated clay of the body shrinks more rapidly than the glaze as the fired porcelain cools. The glaze on the edges, rims, and pointed surfaces flaked off easily, revealing the white, or more usually, grey body underneath. So highly prized were *mushikui* that by the eighteenth century Japanese porcelain potters were faking them.[3] After about 1630, the Jingdezhen potters added ferruginous enamel to the rims of the *ko'akae* wares, creating the brown "dressing" which characterizes many of the polychrome wares in the catalogue.[4] This prevents the glaze on the rim from flaking and was added to Shonzui wares as well.

Another technical flaw which characterizes many wares for the Japanese market and reflects the speed of their manufacture is careless glazing. The glaze might not cover a luted area completely, or it might have been applied in a patchy fashion or have simply shrank, pulling away from a foot ring or bottom during firing. The process left streaks and cracks which fired a dark orange if the body had a high iron content or a lighter orange in the case of a more carefully levigated body. This is a very prevalent characteristic on all but the latest and most finely potted *ko'akae* wares, but I have never seen it described. It is a technical fault which helps identify genuine Japanese-market wares made between 1625 and 1645.

The nature of the foot ring also distinguishes *kosometsuke* and *ko'akae* wares of the late Ming from later copies. Generally, foot rings are shallow and unglazed. They are often undercut, canted inward, and finished with two or three wavy, uneven bevels. On dishes and plates, radiating chatter marks are visible on the bottoms under the glaze; they are particularly common on *kosometsuke* and *kraak* wares. Jingdezhen potters did not bother to remove kiln sand and grit from the foot rings of *kosometsuke* or *ko'akae* wares, even on the most skillfully enameled porcelains (see cat. no. 44). Kiln grit sometimes mars the front as well as the bottoms of *kosometsuke*, *ko'akae*, and *kraak* wares. This roughness was treasured both by the Japanese who purchased these wares and by the Japanese who preserved and collected them so carefully. Foot rings attached to square and

lozenge-shaped dishes were sometimes applied with great care but were often attached completely askew, another characteristic which bespeaks the simple, natural, and spontaneous character of the wares.

A final but hitherto overlooked potting characteristic of *ko'akae* wares, which attests to the speed and carefree quality of their production, should be noted. On *ko'akae* wares produced from about 1635 to 1645, the pressure of the potter's hands or finishing tools is visible on the backs or cavettos of the bowls and dishes, descending in broad rings from the foot ring to the rim. On most domestic Chinese wares, these marks were smoothed and eradicated before the bowl or dish left the wheel. They are particularly obvious on those *ko'akae* wares with marks written in seal script or with a six-character Chenghua (1465–1487) mark on the bottom.

The decoration on *kosometsuke* and *ko'akae* also relates to the new aesthetic of the natural and the spontaneous. Many of the *kosometsuke* in the exhibition are decorated with the lowest quality cobalt, which fired a blue-black. The potters didn't use this quality because they had no other option; thinly potted *kraak* wares of this same period are painted with a luminous blue. Japanese-market wares of unusual shape and size, like the dish in the shape of Mount Fuji (cat. no. 9) and the large gourd dish (cat. no. 21), were painted with brighter, more refined cobalt than other wares produced at the same time. But the vast majority of these porcelains were decorated with cobalt which fired a dark blue. The potters did not bother to purify the domestic cobalt used on low-end domestic wares and export porcelains; it was too time-consuming.

The decorations on most *kosometsuke* wares were outlined with astonishing speed and filled in, also at lightning speed, with broad brushstrokes of medium and dark blue wash (fig. 2). Enamels were also applied very rapidly to the underglaze blue decoration on Tianqi era (1621–1627) *ko'akae* wares (cat. nos. 35, 48, 89). The yellow enamel of this period is yolk-colored, and often minute bubbles are visible where it was thickly applied. These dishes are often decorated on their backs with cobalt-blue sprays embellished with iron-red berries. The Japanese who used these wares were correct to value them for the spontaneity of their decoration as well as the unaffected naturalness of the potting.

Ko'akae wares of the 1630s and early 1640s were more labor-intensive; they required two firings, but the enamels—yellow, green, brown, aubergine, iron red and "black"—had to be relatively carefully applied on top of or within the outlines of the underglaze cobalt blue and the overglaze iron red or "black." The "black" enamel was complicated to apply. It was in fact cobalt oxide painted on top of already glazed porcelain. The cobalt was allowed to dry and covered with green enamel, which was then "fixed" in an oxygen-rich firing which melted the green enamel. Enamels had to be relatively carefully applied within the iron-red outlines (fig. 3) because iron red contained a lead oxide flux which dissolved easily if touched by the other enamels.[5] Careful inspection of later *ko'akae* wares, however, reveals that they too were decorated quickly and with the same assurance that characterized *kosometsuke* wares, if not always with the same restraint.

The trade taste and transformation that this catalogue chronicles took place between about 1620 and

Fig. 3. Three-legged toad of Daoist immortal Liu Haichan (Jp: Gama Sennin), outlined in iron-red enamel. Detail of hexagonal dish (cat. no. 44)

1645 for very specific reasons. Before this period, the Wanli emperor (r. 1573–1620) had come close to bankrupting China by his inability to reform the Ming bureaucracy in times of chronic military crisis. The defense of Korea in the 1590s against two Japanese invasions, whose ultimate target was China, and an attack in 1619 by Nurhachi, leader of the powerful Manchu tribe from northeastern China, were particularly draining. Not until after the Wanli emperor's death in 1620 were the Chinese again officially permitted to trade with Japan. By this time, the potteries at Jingdezhen were suffering hard times and orders from the imperial court had been greatly curtailed. The imperial kiln was shut down, and the potters were looking for new markets to fill the void created by diminished orders from the court. For decades, the potters had produced *kraak* porcelains: busily decorated bowls, dishes, bottles, and boxes for the Portuguese, Spanish, Dutch, Turks, Persians, and South Asians (fig. 4). So finally, after the end of the conflict with Japan and the death of the Wanli emperor, these potters were able to produce wares specifically to Japanese orders and taste. Many *kosometsuke* share potting characteristics with *kraak* wares, including poorly levigated clay, unrefined cobalt which fired blue-black, broad-brush painting, chatter marks, and gritty foot rings.

It should be noted that there are no tea bowls in the exhibition or catalogue. Chinese tea bowls made exclusively for the Japanese market, particularly those large enough for serving the thick tea which was shared by the participants of the tea ceremony, are extremely scarce. Kawahara illustrates more than twenty *kosometsuke* "tea bowls" for serving thin tea;[6] all but a few

have counterparts in the catalogues of the Hatcher cargo, sunk near Singapore around 1643 and sold at Christie's, Amsterdam, in 1984.[7] Bowls for thin, or steeped, tea can also be found at the Topkapi Museum in Istanbul,[8] in early European collections of Chinese export porcelain, or among the shards in the James River basin, where Dutch traders brought porcelains to trade for tobacco with the early settlers of Virginia.[9]

Japanese tea masters have always valued most highly Japanese stoneware tea bowls for serving thick tea. Black or red-brown-glazed Raku ware, coiled not wheel-thrown, heavy black Seto ware, or clog-shaped Oribe ware tea bowls, as Mary Ann Rogers has pointed out in her essay for this catalogue, were prized for this purpose. They were the essence of the *wabi* concept of tea. *Wabi* is often translated to mean "poverty," not in the sense of a lack of material possessions but rather a state of mind that accepts a disciplined and austere existence. *Wabi* tea masters, of which Sen no Rikyū (r. 1522–16201) is the most famous, found beauty in objects of nature, which were naturally and spontaneously produced, and in products of Japanese kilns, not the shiny and almost perfect Chinese Song and Yuan dynasty Jizhou, Jian, and Longquan celadon wares beloved of earlier tea masters. These values influenced the wares of Jingdezhen made for the Japanese market. Rogers further points out that *kosometsuke* are not direct copies of earlier Japanese stonewares; instead, the numerous forms of these stonewares influenced the shapes of *kosometsuke*, as seen in the first section of the exhibition (cat. nos. 1–32).

Accounts of early seventeenth-century tea ceremonies tell us that Japanese tea masters advocated mix-

20

ing their media when serving tea.[10] Porcelain and stoneware incense boxes were used seasonally, not all year around; the types of vessels used varied with the time of day and the season. *Kosometsuke*, and particularly *ko'akae*, wares would have been used with metal, lacquer, wood, and stoneware containers and vessels as accents in the tea ceremony. The sparing use of Chinese porcelains with vessels of other media in the tea ceremony may explain why we do not find more porcelain tea bowls for thick tea, tea jars, or saki ewers and saki cups in the surviving body of *kosometsuke* wares.

It is also important to remember that different classes in Japanese society had different tastes in tea wares and everyday vessels. By the 1630s, the potters of Jingdezhen were making two sorts of wares for the Japanese market. One of these groups continued to express austere and whimsical tea taste, even when judiciously decorated with polychrome enamels. The other group of wares provided consumers of all classes with a "cheap and cheerful" (to steal a phase from Nigel Wood) alternative to *wabi* tea taste (fig. 5). It has been suggested that the potters pro-duced at least some of the *ko'akae* wares, described in Sections III to V of the catalogue, to appeal to the ostentatious taste of Japan's warrior classes. I leave it to scholars more knowledgeable than I about Japan's class structure to sort out which wares would have appealed to whom in early Edo Japan.

The exhibition is divided into five sections, the first (cat. nos. 1–32) composed of forms produced for the Japanese market to be used in the tea ceremony. The second section (cat. nos. 33–44) illustrates decorative schemes which express Japanese taste of the early Edo period, around 1615 to 1645: a love of asymmetry, the use of divided fields or alternating sides (known in Japan as *katami-gawari*), and the love of intensive textile-like patterning to form backgrounds or borders on the porcelains. Borrowed Japanese forms, decorative schemes, and techniques illustrate in the most obvious possible way the trade taste to which the potters of Jingdezhen catered when they produced *kosometsuke* and *ko'akae* wares. The porcelains in this catalogue also illustrate the transformations of Chinese decorative motifs required of

Fig. 4. *Kraak* plate, ca. 1610–1630. Porcelain decorated in underglaze cobalt blue, diam. 20.2 cm. Private collection

21

Fig. 5. Two *ko'akae* dishes from a set of five dishes (*mukozuke*), ca. 1630–1645. Porcelain decorated with enamels, diam. 13.3 cm each. Private collection

Jingdezhen potters producing for the Japanese market.

Among the most treasured of all wares for the Japanese market are the large *kosometsuke* vessels catalogued in Section I. The largest are the water jars (Jp: *mizusashi*) used to hold the fresh water that went into the iron kettle which provided the hot water for making tea. A water jar decorated with large tree peony blossoms and four lion dogs (cat. no. 4) is a perfect example of the Chinese potters' attempts to accomodate market demands early in the first decade of direct trade with Japan. At that time, the potters received orders for vessels whose functions they hardly understood. The Chinese used buckets to draw water from streams or huge, thick ceramic jars to store water for tea; they worried mostly about the source of the water (snow or streams), not the aesthetics of its storage. This water jar surprised me when I saw it. The vessel itself could only have been made for Japan as a water jar. Its tall shape, wide rim decorated on both sides, and highly decorated border placed down inside the jar proclaim its function. The pattern which decorates the jar is also found on *kraak* wares and is derived from decoration on Wanli domestic wares. Its densely decorated surface differs from those of most of the water jars illustrated in Masahiko Kawahara's *Kosometsuke* volumes and does not accord with modern-day concepts of *wabi* tea taste.[11] But it certainly echoes the taste of some Japanese textiles of the period and the *ko'akae* wares produced in the 1630s and early 1640s.

The water jar in the form of a bucket (cat. no. 3) is another object of singular shape to the Chinese potter. A porcelain copy of a very humble object, it accords better with the Japanese concept of *wabi*. Its overall decoration of fish, sea creatures, and sea grasses is very typical of late Wanli porcelains made for the domestic market and harks back to the early Ming. Here again, the potters used a familiar set of motifs to decorate a unique, very foreign shape. Another water jar, its cylindrical sides painted with horses and its original lid decorated with a landscape (cat. no 17), fits perfectly the *wabi* concept of tea and is notable for the wonderful use of undecorated or negative space which characterizes many of the most striking *kosometsuke* wares. The fact that this water pot has retained its original lid bespeaks the value and care bestowed on this object by its previous owners in Japan. Unlike many containers made by Jingdezhen potters for the Chinese market over the ages, the rims of these and similar water jars are inverted and glazed, so they don't look so stunted without a porcelain lid. I suspect that many if not most of the *mizusashi* illustrated in Masahiko Kawahara's encyclopedic volumes had similar lids and are now making do with lacquer or metal substitutes. The porcelain ladle from the Leventritt Collection at the Asian Art Museum, which might have been made to accompany a water jar, is also an extraordinarily rare survival. Whether it was made actually to be used is difficult to say, but it could certainly have been marveled at by guests at a tea ceremony.

The second largest vessels in the exhibition are two ewers (cat. nos. 2, 6), one of which is in the form of a wine pot or kettle with bail handle (cat. no. 2). These are known in Japanese as *mizutsugi*, literally "water replenishment pitchers." Like their Oribe ware predecessors, they were used to replenish the *mizusashi* with water "during the latter part of the tea ceremony"; their spouts directed the water "accurately" into the *mizusashi*. [12] These two *mizutsugi* ewers illustrate contrasting impulses in the origins of wares for the Japanese market. The hexagonal ewer is based on the wine pot which the Chinese also made for themselves and for the southeast Asian and European markets. [13] It is painted in broad brushstrokes with beguiling water buffalo in a variety of postures: one with its head and body on the pot but its tail end on the lid; another looks out curiously at the beholder (fig. 6). The plain ground of the pot focuses our eye on the oxen, a favorite Chan (Jp: Zen) Buddhist topic, popular in China in the Southern Song and Yuan dynasties (1127–1368) and transmitted to Buddhist Japan where it was popular for even longer. The second water replenishment pitcher is decorated with a typical Chinese theme: scholars, carrying the parasol which distinguishes them as having passed at least two of their examinations for the emperors' civil service, and small boys, future scholars, cavorting in a celestial garden. The shape and size of the ewer tells us that it was made for the Japanese market, specifically for the tea ceremony. It has an inverted unglazed rim that was meant to be covered, and the proportions of the body lead one to believe that it would have had a flat lacquer or bronze lid.

Another object made for the tea ceremony is the incense container (Jp: *kōgō*), which was used to hold incense added to the charcoal in the brazier and/or to be placed in the *tokonoma*, an alcove in the Japanese tea room, for the admiration of guests. Although one of the smallest objects of the tea equipage, the *kōgō* has always been ranked as a most precious possession, and very few are seen in the West. In the mid-nineteenth century, a list of champion *kōgō* was made up, much like the lists ranking sumo wrestlers; numerous Chinese porcelain *kōgō* made the list. A small Jingdezhen porcelain box in the form of a Shinto shrine, *tsujido*, with a pyramid-shaped lid decorated with autumn leaves shared first place on the list with a tiny green-glazed southern Chinese stoneware box in the shape of a turtle. [14] Today, ceramic *kōgō* are used from November through April, wood and lacquer in late spring, summer, and early fall. *Kōgō* of metal, shell, and similar materials are not limited by season. [15]

The exhibition includes four incense containers, one an elegant square *kōgō* in the shape of a bridge piling decorated with diaper patterns (cat. no. 15). A tiny box with the figure of a water buffalo on top (cat. no. 11) and two

kōgō in animal forms, one an upright snail (cat. no. 14) and the other a quail (cat. no. 12), complete the group made specifically for Japanese *chajin*, or "tea men." The latter two examples are related in feeling to the unique dishes which the Chinese potters created in animal and vegetable shapes, to be discussed shortly. A small box decorated with a horse (cat. no. 13) is included in the exhibition to represent a "discovered" object, an object not specifically made for the Japanese market but adopted for use in the tea ceremony. This small box was made to contain red seal paste for a literate Chinese, who would have pressed his seal into the paste and then onto a document, painting, or calligraphy. The body of the little horse-decorated box is different from other porcelains in the exhibition. Its painting resembles the decoration on a large group of very crude dishes retrieved from the Hatcher cargo mentioned above. [16]

Other forms in Section I of this catalogue owe their origin directly or indirectly to Japanese ceramics: basket-

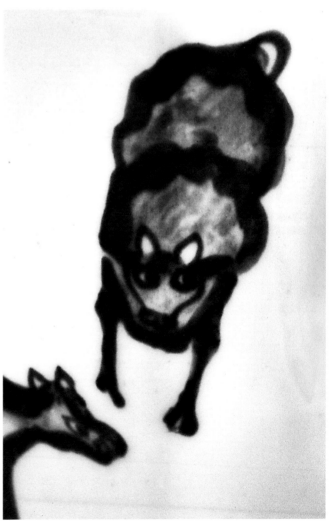

Fig. 6. Figure of water buffalo. Detail of hexagonal ewer (cat. no. 2)

23

shaped dishes (Jp: *tebachi*), thick footed dishes, and tall food vessels (Jp: *mukozuke*). The two *tebachi* in the exhibition (cat. nos. 5, 18) are based on Oribe and Bizen prototypes and would have been used to serve food during the *kaiseki* meal of the full tea ceremony. The handles on the Oribe prototypes are a good deal more elaborately potted than most surviving Chinese porcelain baskets illustrated in Kawahara or elsewhere, but that may be because firing cracks prematurely weakened the handles of porcelain examples. Japanese stoneware examples may have had more structural integrity than the hastily potted versions from Jingdezhen. These baskets and the large dishes, some of which would also have been used as tea wares, were made in the same way as their Japanese prototypes, that is, with strips of clay luted onto thick slabs of clay to form the sides and bottoms of the vessel. The remarkable dishes in the form of Mount Fuji (cat. no. 9), the gourd-shaped dish (cat. no. 10), and the double gourd dish (cat. no. 21) are examples of this transformation. Like their Oribe counterparts, they have applied U-shaped feet. These large slab-formed porcelains may also be ultimately related to the flat lacquer trays used for food service in the tea ceremony. Three large plates (cat. nos. 20, 78, 104) in the exhibition must also have been based on Japanese stoneware prototypes; they are very heavy and have thick, shallow foot rings. A plate decorated with two women, a flowering tree, and small boys also has rim decoration copied from Oribe ware (see entry for cat. no. 78), and a deep bowl decorated with a landscape (cat. no. 81) is directly based on an Oribe ware form. Finally, there are two tall food dishes in the exhibition that are evocative of Japanese stonewares without being copies. One, a small bowl decorated with water buffalo (cat. no. 23), is made for serving bits of food. The other, a *mukozuke* in the form of a lotus flower (cat. no. 7), is particularly reminiscent of Oribe dishes made in the form of chrysanthemum flowers but is also actually deeper.[17]

One other object relates directly to the tea ceremony. The charcoal container (cat. nos. 16, 66) was a new form to the potters of Jingdezhen and was even relatively new to Japan. These containers, which worked very well in heavily potted porcelain, were made to hold ash with a piece of burning charcoal on top. Guests used the charcoal to light the long pipes placed on the tobacco tray (Jp: *tabako-bon*) in the waiting area where they sat before the tea ceremony began. The charcoal containers are heavily potted on the bottom and sides and can be round, hexagonal, octagonal, or irregularly shaped. They are, alas, easy to confuse with tea bowls unless you can inspect them carefully.

Historians do not know much about the transmission of orders in commercial trade. The most intriguing of the objects generally acknowledged to have been ordered for Japanese tea masters are the unique dishes (Jp: *mukozuke*) made in sets of five, ten, or more in the shape of objects of great cultural importance, like the lute or the fan, or in animal, vegetal, floral, and even human shapes (cat. nos. 24–32). While we can infer much about the transmission of shapes and decoration from the wares themselves, no one knows how these dishes came to be produced. Kawahara illustrates over sixty different shapes of these food dishes.[18] The majority of those in the form of birds, beasts, vegetables, or flowers, as well as the rare human figure (fig. 7), were made at the same kilns; they share the same potting characteristics and clay color, and many are similarly decorated on the back with outlines, molded detail, and often *fukizumi* ("blown ink," or *soufflé* blue), a technique also appearing occasionally on wares for the domestic market. These *mukozuke* are dishes in entirely new forms, never before produced in China. Their astonishing diversity reveals the inventiveness of Jingdezhen's potters and the wit of the tea masters who have treasured them for centuries. The dishes themselves reveal the lengths to which Chinese potters in the 1620s would go to meet the demands of a new market. It is just possible that these wares may have been inspired by Oribe ware *kōgō*, which were occasionally fashioned in the form of animals, plants, and "man-made objects."[19]

The second section in the exhibition represents decoration unique to the Japanese market and is a key to the decoration on many of the dishes and plates in the rest of the exhibition. Not only did the Chinese potters create shapes unique to the Japanese market, but they also used decorative devices antithetical to Chinese aesthetics and very much in vogue around the first half of the seventeenth century in late Momoyama (1573–1615) and early Edo (1615–1868) Japan. These devices include the use of asymmetry in border design and the composition of a central scene, the use of divided fields or contrasting grounds (Jp: *katami-gawari*), and the use of diaper patterning associated with textile design. Rondels were a particularly popular Japanese decorative device; borders were often decorated part way around with rondels of abstract or floral patterns (see cat. no. 34). The use of a chevron and a petal pattern in only the top third of a border is particularly striking, especially when paired with a particularly Japanese theme, the gathering of brine to turn into salt (cat. no. 36). Two small dishes in the exhibition illustrate the use of *katami-gawari*, which characterize so many of the striking "Kyoto-style" Oribe wares of red and white clay with green glaze, white slip, and iron glaze. It is also a popular device on Kodaiji lacquer.[20] In one of the dishes (cat. no. 39), two designs are separated by a line through the middle, like many of the lacquer wares. On the second dish (cat. no. 38), potter-painters have used the white ground of the porcelain to divide two separate decorations. The asymmetrical placement of flowers or scenes over the entire surface of the dish would not have appealed to Chinese consumers but was still skillfully employed by Jingdezhen potters. One dish is decorated with asymmetrical chrysanthemum flowers, leaves, and a hidden design (Ch: *an hua*) of chrysanthemum blossoms, almost like a Japanese textile, and is a tour de force of the potter's art (cat. no. 37). And a *ko'akae* dish with its design canted to the upper right and lower left (cat. no. 40) is reminiscent of the Southern Song (1127–1279) fan paintings beloved of the Japanese. Finally, the extensive use of diaper patterns—as borders (cat. no. 44), as a ground for other decoration (cat. no. 41), or as an adaptation of an actual textile design (cat. no. 43)—is antithetical to Chinese taste but typical of the patternization found in Japanese decorative arts of the early Edo period.

The subtle interaction of the two cultures is evident in the decoration on the numerous small porcelain dishes that survive in Japan and elsewhere. Here we see trade taste expressed in the arrangement of the decoration on porcelains, and we see a transformation occurring when certain of the decorative schemes are interpreted in the light of Japanese culture. In the late sixteenth and early seventeenth century, Japanese cuisine was enjoying a period of development and refinement which must have increased demand for plates and dishes of all sorts. Dishes made and sold in groups of five, ten, and even twenty would have been used for meals, including the meal which accompanied the tea ceremony. A few Oribe ware examples of these sets survive, but Japanese art historians refer to these Oribe wares as "ordinary tableware," not made for the tea ceremony. Some of the porcelain plates and dishes in the exhibition were also ordinary tableware. But in the 1620s and 1630s, glazed stonewares and Chinese porcelains were luxury items used only by "members of the elite," no matter whether aristocrat, warrior, or merchant.[21]

Designs on the porcelains in the last three sections of the catalogue are heavily drawn from Chinese motifs and iconography or are shared by the cultures of both China and Japan. In a few instances, the Chinese decoration took on different meaning in Japan. The third section (cat. nos. 45–65) deals with themes of nature;

Fig. 7. Bottom of dish (*mukozuke*) in the form of a man (cat. no. 26). His facial features are outlined and his midriff is decorated with *fukizumi*, "blown ink." Kiln grit adheres to the unglazed bottoms of the four feet and a gold lacquer repair is visible on his robe

plants and animals that decorate many of the dishes and plates made for Japan, some used for the tea ceremony. Love of nature has undergirded religion and society in both countries long before recorded history and is particularly evident on the dishes, bowls, and plates painted with plants, animals, and landscapes.

The Chinese floral and faunal motifs used to decorate the *ko'akae* dishes and blue-and-white dishes and plates in Section III are often rebuses, or verbal puns, popular with the Chinese imperial court. Most of the dishes in this section are decorated with rebuses containing wishes for promotion and for larger emoluments in the Chinese emperor's civil service administration (see cat. nos. 46, 53, 55). A small square dish probably used for pickles or other condiments (cat. no. 50) also illustrates a Japanese rebus; the Japanese word for "mandarin duck," *oshidori*, is a homophone for the two-syllable phrase, "to take authority," and so the image also expresses congratulations or a wish for advancement. Two groups of dishes in this exhibition probably had particular meaning for the military classes in Japan: those decorated with falcons and those decorated with fighting cocks (cat. nos. 63, 64). By the Edo period (1615–1868), the falcon had become a symbol of the "warrior class" and the fighting cock was an emblem of the fighting spirit so highly valued after a century of wars in Japan. The scenes on four dishes in this section (cat. nos. 46, 47, 49, 65) are based on illustrations from *Caobenhua shipu*, volume six of the eight-volume Chinese woodblock-printed book *Bazhong huapu* [Manual of Eight Styles of Painting] (Jp: *Hasshu gafu*), printed in the Tianqi period (1621–1627) and popular in Japan as well.[22] Both the Japanese and the Chinese shared an interest in seasonal floral symbols. Thus the pine, bamboo, and prunus were symbols of the New Year, the willow and cherry blossom were signs of spring, and the chrysanthemum was emblematic of autumn in Japan. These associations with particular seasons must have dictated the use to which these porcelains were put in and out of the tea hut. Finally, I hope it has not escaped notice that although many of these dishes are decorated with motifs also popular in China, such as horses, deer, pine, and other plants and animals, the potters arranged them in ways which they hoped would appeal to Japanese taste. Many of the animals and flowers occupy the entire surface of the dish or plate and are silhouetted against a sparsely decorated ground; the sparseness of decoration makes the flowers and figures pop out at the beholder. The swift broad-brush painting also endows them with boldness and immediacy unique to Jingdezhen porcelains made for Japan.

The fourth section of the exhibition (cat. nos. 66–88) is devoted to Chinese themes and is divided between images of the particular scholar and images of the generalized scholar as icon. It reflects the pre-eminent role of the scholar in Chinese society, a role not exactly analogous to that of the scholar in Japan. This section also contains porcelains decorated with landscapes, traditionally associated with the scholar and the themes of reclusion and self-cultivation. Decorated with very Chinese themes, these dishes and plates are examples of the transformation affected by Jingdezhen potters for the Japanese market; the weird scale, skewed ground planes, and lack of perspective on these dishes and plates characterize the particular scenes painted on most *kosometsuke* and *ko'akae* wares.

The square, hexagonal, and octagonal *ko'akae* dishes made for the Japanese market in the1630s were perfect vehicles for depicting the particular scholar. Wang Xizhi, China's most noted calligrapher, and Zhou Dunyi, China's first neo-Confucian cosmologist and author of

an essay celebrating the lotus, are each pictured in a garden setting (cat. nos. 67, 68). A set of five *ko'akae* dishes depicts the young boy (a future scholar) with an adult scholar at leisure in nature (cat. no. 71). Two dishes depict small boys at play in a garden; they are emblematic of the happiness that all Chinese families wished for, to have noble sons, *guizi*, who would pass the emperor's civil service examinations, receive a lucrative appointment from the emperor, and support their families on income from land bought with their official salaries (cat. nos. 71, 77). A small pickle dish is decorated with the first scholar in the land, the successful candidate who earned first place in the imperial civil service (cat. no. 70). Scholars often traveled to sacred or scenic sites, and as officials, they were always posted to areas distant from their ancestral districts; so they are often pictured on journeys. The scholar is depicted as a solitary fisherman as well as an intrepid traveler. One of the most curious depictions in the catalogue is that of four scholars in a mountainous setting, probably the Four Greybeards of the Shang Mountains. The Four Greybeards and the Seven Sages of the Bamboo Grove, two groups of Chinese scholar-gentry who courageously defied the political conventions of their times, were the most frequently depicted icons in Japanese painting during the late seventeenth century (see cat. entry no. 76).

The landscapes which decorate porcelains in the fourth section became the classic expression of the Chinese scholar-elite by the tenth century, partly because the subject provided the scholar-painter with the opportunity to show off his calligraphic brushstrokes. Also, remote natural settings were the most prestigious places for Chinese scholars to carry on their self-cultivation: reading, writing, practicing their calligraphy, and holding scholarly gatherings where they would write poetry and drink tea or wine with other highly educated men. Some of the landscapes on *kosometsuke* mimic the landscapes conventions on contemporary domestic porcelains (cat. nos. 79, 80). Some represent late sixteenth-century archaistic landscape conventions, with recession indicated by mountains stacked one on top of another (cat. no. 82). Others, use receding ground planes to indicate distance (cat. no. 81). The pines on many of these dishes and plates are given special character by the slapdash painting of their angular forms and the odd placement of needles and trailing vines. These special pines are quite uncommon on domestic porcelains and lend a strange charm to wares for the Japanese market. The hexagonal charcoal container in this exhibition (cat. no. 66) illustrates a perfect example of a landscape decoration devised to suit the Japanese market; the clouds are painted in an archaistic fashion known in Japan as "pavilions among swirling clouds," used to decorate bowls like one known to have been owned by the great tea master Sen no Rikyū.[23]

The last three plates in this section of the catalogue were probably produced in the 1630s and represent creations for Japanese taste in both style and substance. On one plate (cat. no 87), the highly abstract depiction of the "three friends of winter," each separated from the other through the very effective use of negative or blank space, is different from their representation on Chinese domestic porcelains. The hemp palm on the second plate (cat. no. 86) is seldom depicted in Chinese art; the unusual linking of the tree with a flying book and a Buddhist pine-bark-shaped lozenge must have been inspired by Japanese imagery. On the third plate (cat. no. 88), the raft in the process of disintegration also represents a very Japanese concern with the iconography and decorative possibility of utilitarian objects, also seen in the use of a bridge piling as inspiration for a tiny incense container (cat. no. 15). The latter two plates probably express Buddhist themes: palms were often planted at Buddhist monasteries, the book represents the Buddhist law, and the disintegrating raft expresses the ephemeral nature of human existence.

Daoist and Buddhist themes are the final category (cat. nos. 89–104) of decoration on *kosometsuke* and *ko'akae* wares. The transmission of Daoism to Japan is extremely complex; it may have come into Japan through Korea as well from China. In the seventh and early eighth century, Japan adopted the Chinese legal and administrative system. A special Bureau of *Yin* and *Yang* (Jp: *Iny-oryo*) was established to track and manage cosmology and astronomy, to calculate calendars, and to regulate time keeping. In the tenth century, *yin-yang* divination was popular with the aristocracy for telling personal fortunes and was used with spells and rituals to ward off danger and bad luck, becoming a religious practice known as *inyodo*.[24] Esoteric, or Tantric Buddhism, a branch of *Mahayana* Buddhism, which came to Japan in the ninth century, was growing in influence at the same time. Esoteric Buddhism posited the here and now rather than eternity and offered a variety of incantations, charms, and rituals for specific threats and circumstances. Thus, by the tenth century, elements of Daoist belief and practice melded with Buddhism and the pre-existing beliefs and ritual practices of *yin-yang* divination.[25]

By the early seventeenth century, the Japanese who used these porcelains would have been familiar with the Eight Daoist Immortals and Daoist practices, incantations, and divination. Perhaps because of the size of the small dishes produced for the Japanese market, the Eight Immortals seldom appear together, but they do appear singly or in groups of three or four (see cat. no. 92). The Five Ancients representing the Five Elements, codified in Chinese popular religion and Daoism as the essential ingredients of earthly life—earth, fire, water, metal, and wood—appear on these wares (cat. nos. 91, 96). Their Daoist connections are made clear by the fact that they are depicted gazing at a handscroll depicting the Three Terraces constellation (cat. no. 91), which Daoists believe regulates human affairs, and at the *taiji* diagram (cat. no. 96), which represents the union of the opposing elements *yin* and *yang* as well as the unity of the *Dao*. Individual Daoist immortals (Ch: *xian*; Jp: *sennin*) decorate dishes, plates, and other vessels made for the Japanese. Lü Dongbin often appears on these porcelains; he is the most popular of the Eight Immortals in China (cat. no. 93). The Daoists Liu Hai (cat. no. 90) and Li Tieguai, two rather grotesque figures, are painted with the two Buddhist poet-monks Hanshan (Jp: Kanzan) and Shide (Jp: Jittoku) on a small square dish (cat. no. 97). Chinese popular religion is conflated with Daoism on a plate decorated with the Eight Trigrams and the white hare who pounds the elixir of immortality with Chang'e on the moon (cat. no. 94). The Jade Hare represents a motif transferred from Jingdezhen to the Japanese potter in Arita. And a figure which may represent the rain master Yushi, a popular Chinese god who was incorporated into Daoist imagery by the fourteenth century, appears on a *ko'akae* dish (cat. no. 89).[26] This particular dish is part of a group of small dishes made for Japan, decorated with figures in underglaze blue with added polychrome enamels. Most have four-character Tianqi marks; many later copies of these wares exist.

Also popular were Buddhist subjects, some rather covert like the hemp palms (see cat. no. 86) and a raft depicted in the process of disintegrating (see cat. no. 88). Individual Buddhist lohans and persons in the "unofficial status category" of Chan (Jp: Zen) Buddhist hagiographies, like the Tang Buddhist monk-poets Hanshan and Shide (cat. nos. 97, 98), are depicted on *kosometsuke* and *ko'akae* wares. Bodhidharma (Ch: Damo; Jp: Daruma), who is credited with bringing Chan Buddhism from India to China in the late sixth century, is depicted on bowls, plates, and a charcoal container in Masahiko Kawahara's encyclopedic volume on *kosometsuke*, but his image is not included in this catalogue.[27] The small dishes made in sets of five, ten, or more were perfect vehicles for portraying seated lohans (cat. nos. 99, 100), many of indeterminate identity because they lack attributes, such as fly whisks, books, and beads, or identifying hand gestures known as mudra. The popular Chinese god of happiness Budai (Jp: Hotei) is a manifestation of Maitreya, Buddha of the future. Depicted on numerous small dishes as a begging monk seated contentedly on a mat with his large stomach exposed, he looks every bit the happy role in which he was cast (cat. nos. 101, 102).

Large elephants decorate the last two dishes pictured in the catalogue (cat. nos. 103, 104). This animal is highly important as the vehicle of the bodhisattva Samantabhadra, protector of Buddhist law, and of the law itself; the elephant thus came to symbolize the vehicle for the propagation of the Buddhist faith.[28] But the elephant is rarely depicted on *kosometsuke* or *ko'akae* wares. The footed dish in the form of a chrysanthemum (cat. no. 103), probably made in the 1630s, is a serious depiction of Buddhist iconography. Here a white elephant is outfitted with a cloth embellished with a tortoiseshell pattern of hexagons containing blossoms. On top of the cloth sits a footed lotus; an aura emanates from the lotus and in its midst is a book of scripture or a reliquary. The figure of the pristine elephant is perched on a rocky pedestal suspended in a void, completely removed form the ephemeral world of humanity. A second elephant decorates another dish (cat. no. 104), which must have been based on a Japanese stoneware prototype; this leads one to suspect that at least a few Japanese stonewares must have been sent to the potters of Jingdezhen as models. This is a jaunty elephant, painted during the first decade of direct trade with Japan. It waves a lotus, Buddhist symbol of purity, in its trunk. On the surface, this dish depicts a serious religious subject, and the eloquent use of negative space would have made it suitable for use in the tea ceremony. For the Chinese, however, the elephant mounted by a young boy would have had a second meaning; the Chinese word for "elephant" is *xiang*, which is a homophone for a word meaning "auspicious," *jixiang*, "to mount an elephant," is thus a rebus for the compound word meaning "auspicious." So the dish would have conveyed a wish of propitious events, perhaps, because of the boy mounting the elephant, a wish for the arrival of sons.

The sections dividing this exhibition were arrived at deductively from the nature of the porcelains themselves and represent a rather basic analytical framework. This approach was made necessary by the fact that relatively little has been written about the wares themselves in any language. Furthermore, primary source records of trade, such as the vast archives of the British and Dutch East India Companies that revealed so much about the nature of porcelain trade with the West, are not available for trade between China and Japan. And no shipwrecks, such as the *Witte Leeuw*, White Lion, of 1613 and the Hatcher wreck of around 1643, have been discovered which would shed light on the *kosometsuke* and *ko'akae* wares traded with Japan between 1620 and 1640. Lacking such primary and secondary sources for the Japanese trade, it has been critical to closely examine and analyze the wares themselves; this process has resulted in the new findings presented in this essay and the catalogue which follows. The porcelains in Sections I and II in this catalogue reveal the direct influence of Japanese taste on the porcelains ordered for the tea ceremony and for use as everyday wares. The creation of shapes hitherto totally unknown to the Chinese potter bespeaks their ingenuity and flexibility in attempting to meet trade taste. The porcelains in Sections III to V of the catalogue reveal the way the potters of Jingdezhen were able to adapt traditional Chinese decorative motifs to suit what they thought was Japanese taste. These adaptations exemplify just how different the *kosometsuke* and *ko'akae* wares are from export porcelains produced for any other market. Stephen Little astutely observes in his essay for this catalogue that "As manifestations of enormous creativity in times of hardship, [*kosometsuke* and *ko'akae* wares] survive as unique symbols of human strength and endurance."

At a moment when the potters of Jingdezhen sought additional markets, the Japanese were not yet producing porcelain. So the twenty-year period of trade between China and Nagasaki enabled the Japanese to take advantage of Jingdezhen's incredibly efficient mass production techniques, including the cost-saving use of poorly levigated clay and inferior cobalt, to obtain porcelains produced to their taste, complete with such technical faults as *mushikui*, which they have treasured ever since. The brilliance of the best *ko'akae*, mass-produced though they were, must have dazzled Japanese consumers and perhaps influenced some of the splendid polychrome-decorated porcelains which the Japanese later produced. Most of all, *kosometsuke* and *ko'akae* wares reveal the astonishing scale of the Jingdezhen potters' repertoire and their consummate ability to transform their own production and adapt it to trade taste, creating the most humorous, whimsical, and beautiful export wares of their long history.

NOTES

1. Stephen Little, "Ko-sometsuke in the Asian Art Museum of San Francisco," *Orientations* 13 (April 1982), pp. 12–23; Yoshiko Kakudo, *The Effie B. Allison Collection: Kosometsuke and other Chinese Blue-and-White Porcelains* (San Francisco: Asian Art Museum, 1982); Barbara Harrisson, *Chinese Porcelain: the Transitional Period, 1620–1683, A Selection from the Michael Butler Collection* (Leeuwarden: Princessehof Museum, 1986); Richard Kilburn, *Transitional Wares and Their Forerunners* (Hong Kong: Oriental Ceramic Society of Hong Kong, 1981); Herbert Butz and Kawahara Masahiko, eds., *Chinesische Porzellane des 17. Jahrhunderts für Japan: Sammlung Georg Weishaupt* (Berlin: Museum für Ostasiatische Kunst, 1996).

2. Kawahara Masahiko, "Chinese Ceramic Exports to Japan: The Legacy of Blue and White Porcelain and Porcelain with Five Color Decoration of the Seventeenth Century," translated into German by Bernard Riessland, in Butz and Kawahara, *Chinesische Porzellane des 17. Jahrhunderts für Japan*, p. 26. [Essay and catalogue translated into English by Frauke Carlucci.] For examples of Shonzui ware, see Seizo Hayashiya and Henry Trubner, et al., *Chinese Ceramics from Japanese Collections: T'ang through Ming Dynasties* (New York: Asia Society, 1977), nos. 70–74.

3. Kawahara Masahiko, *Ko-sometsuke*, vol. 2, *Monochrome Section* (Kyoto: Kyoto Shoin, 1977), p. 216. [English translation of essay, pp. 209–34, by Meghen Jones, Wakana Kikuchi, and Jonathan Chaves.]

4. Margaret Medley, "Trade, Craftsmanship and Decoration," in Michael Butler et al., *Seventeenth-Century Chinese Porcelain from the Butler Family Collection* (Alexandria, Virginia: Art Services International, 1990), p. 15.

5. Nigel Wood, *Chinese Glazes: Their Origins, Chemistry, and Recreation* (London: A. and C. Black; Philadelphia: University of Pennsylvania Press, 1999), p. 235.

6. Kawahara, *Ko-sometsuke*, vol. 2, *Monochrome Section*, pp. 129–40. See ibid., pp. 53–59, for examples of Chinese tea bowls made for serving thick tea. Based on sets of Oribe wares in similar shapes, the "cylinder shape tea cups" that Kawahara illustrates are in fact food dishes (*mukozuke*); ibid., nos. 232–46. See Miyeko Murase, ed., *Turning Point: Oribe and the Arts of Sixteenth-Century Japan* (New York: Metropolitan Museum of Art, 2003), nos. 84, 86, 87.

7. Christie's Amsterdam B.V, *Fine and important late Ming and transitional porcelain recently recovered from an Asian vessel in the South China Sea* (Amsterdam, 14 March 1984), lot nos. 452, 457, 461, 483.

8. Regina Krahl et al., *Chinese Ceramics in the Topkapi Saray Museum, Istanbul: A Complete Catalogue*, vol. 2, *Yuan and Ming Dynasty Porcelains* (London: Sotheby's Publications, 1986), cat nos. 1541, 1543, 1545, 1551–52, 1572–81.

9. Julia B. Curtis, "17th and 18th-Century Chinese Export Ware in Southeastern Virginia," *Transactions of the Oriental Ceramic Society* 53 (1988–89), pp. 47–53.

10. Jun'ichi Takeuchi, "Tea Utensils before Oribe," in Murase, *Turning Point*, p. 32; Jun'ichi Takeuchi, "Furuta Oribe and the Tea Ceremony," in ibid., pp. 17–29.

11. Kawahara, *Ko-sometsuke*, vol. 2, *Monochrome Section*, nos. 145–78.

12. Sen'ō Tanaka and Sendō Tanaka, *The Tea Ceremony*, rev. ed. (Tokyo, New York; London, Kodansha International, 2000), p. 175; Murase, *Turning Point*, p. 177.

13. See Maura Rinaldi, *Kraak Porcelain: A Moment in the History of Trade* (London: Bamboo Publishing, 1989), pp. 182–84, for examples of wine pots.

14. The *kosometsuke kōgō* is now in the Goto Art Museum. See Hayashiya and Trubner, *Chinese Ceramics from Japanese Collections*, p. 110, no. 63, for an illustration and an account of the nineteenth-century ranking of *kōgō*. The turtle *kōgō* is in the Nezu Museum. See Hiroko Nishida, "Collecting Chinese Ceramics in Japan," in "The History of Collecting Oriental Ceramics in East and West," *Vormen uit Vuur* 191/192 (2005, no. 2–3), p. 35, fig. 5.

15. Murase, *Turning Point*, p. 140.

16. Rinaldi, *Kraak Porcelain*, p. 111, plate 109.

17. See, for example, Kawahara, *Ko-sometsuke*, vol. 2, *Monochrome Section*, nos. 351–65; and Murase, *Turning Point*, no. 85.

18. Ibid., nos. 692–757.

19. Murase, *Turning Point*, p. 140, no. 62.

20. Ibid., nos. 64–67, 75, for examples of *katami-gawari* on Oribe ware; and nos. 143–45, 147, for examples of *katami-gawari* on Kodaiji lacquer.

21. Ibid., pp. 173–74.

22. I am indebted to Herbert Butz for his identification of the sources of his nos. 38, 39, 50 in Butz and Kawahara, *Chinesische Porzellane*, pp. 73, 75, 91.

23. Hayashiya and Trubner, *Chinese Ceramics from Japanese Collections*, p. 87, no. 46.

24. Masuo Shin'ichirō, "Daoism in Japan," in Livia Kohn, ed., *The Daoist Handbook* (Leiden: Brill, 2000), pp. 822, 825.

25. Daoist texts were also well known in Japan. A number of ancient manuscripts at the Todaiji Temple Treasure House in Nara and at very old temples in Kyoto contain texts which "can be matched, more or less closely with texts in the Daoist canon." Masuo Shin'ichirō, "Daoism in Japan," pp. 832–33.

26. Stephen Little with Shawn Eichman, *Taoism and the Arts of China* (Chicago: Art Institute of Chicago, 2000), pp. 238–39.

27. Kawahara, *Ko-sometsuke*, vol. 2, *Monochrome Section*, nos. 383, 437, 438, 559, 560, 566. For a short history of Buddhism in Japan, see Robert K. Heinemann, "This World and the Other Power: Contrasting Paths to Deliverance in Japan," in Heinz Bechert and Richard Gombrich, eds., *The World of Buddhism: Buddhist Monks and Nuns in Society and Culture* (London: Thames and Hudson, 1984), pp. 212–30.

28. Merrily Baird, *Symbols of Japan: Thematic Motifs in Art and Design* (New York: Rizzoli International Publications, 2001), pp. 135–36.

Overleaf (detail, cat. no. 33)
Plate
Ming dynasty, Tianqi mark and period (1621–1627)
Porcelain decorated in underglaze cobalt blue
H. 2.3 cm; Diam. 14.6 cm
Private Collection

CATALOGUE

Julia B. Curtis

1. Ladle

青花桃纹水勺

Ming dynasty, ca. 1630–1645
Porcelain decorated in underglaze cobalt blue
L. 17.8 cm
Lent by the Asian Art Museum,
  Gift of Roy Leventritt (B69P101L)

This rare ladle may have been made to scoop water from a fresh water jar during the tea ceremony. But given its fragile nature, it could have been made simply for the admiration of participants in the ceremony. The handle is decorated with the same scrollwork used on the handle of the water jar painted with oxen (cat. no. 2) and may have been done by the same hand. Painted on the middle of the handle is a spiky chrysanthemum flower like those used to decorate the water jar painted with oxen and the dish with foliated rim, chrysanthemum spray, and textile patterns (cat. no. 37). The interior of the ladle is decorated with two peaches, which symbol-ize immortality and are an attribute of Shou Lao (Jp: Jurojin), the Chinese god of longevity. In Japan, Jurojin is often conflated with Fukurokuju, both of whom represent wisdom and learning as well as longevity.[1] In keeping with the aesthetic taste of the Japanese, the peaches are arranged asymmetrically in the ladle's bowl, which is itself subtly shaped like a peach. The finial on the handle probably represents a peach blossom.

The ladle was fired on five spurs, four on the back of the bowl and one on the handle just above the bowl. Six marks are visible on the ladle's bottom; the end of the handle also formed a support. The removal of the spurs revealed a grey body of not too carefully levigated clay. Tiny pinholes pierce the thick glaze of blue-grey tint. The cobalt pigment is of reasonably good quality, and the peaches are painted with some care; graded washes provide some three-dimensionality to the fruit.

1. Merrily Baird, *Symbols of Japan: Thematic Motifs in Art and Design* (New York: Rizzoli Publications, 2001), pp. 199–200.

painted the oxen on the small bowl from the Allison Collection (cat. no. 23); he has depicted their cloven hooves, the folds of their necks, and their quizzical facial expressions, albeit impressionistically.

In China, the water buffalo is the second animal of the zodiac; it pulls the plow and, particularly in southern China, is honored as a symbol of spring. In Chan (Jp: Zen) Buddhism, the herdboy's task of taming and controlling oxen is analogous to setting one's heart/mind at peace through religious discipline; "taming the ox of the mind" was a favorite theme of Chinese and Japanese painters. And in Japan, the ox's ability to ward off smallpox made the animal a talisman against diseases.[3]

Like the handle of the ladle from the Leventritt Collection (cat. no. 1), the ewer's spout is painted with a chrysanthemum and tendrils. Its handle is decorated on the top with a border of blossoms (four chrysanthemums and a peony) and tendrils. Both sides of the handle and the foot are decorated with the same border of scrolling tendrils.

The white clay of the heavily-potted ewer is full of impurities, which has caused pinholes on the body, inside and out, and on the lid. The body was made in two sections and luted together. It is covered on the inside and outside, as well as inside the lid, with a thick greenish-blue glaze. Large bits of kiln grit adhere to the wide, hexagonal foot, which is undercut and beveled very hastily. A firing crack cuts across one side of the foot. The bottom is slightly convex. *Mushikui*, Japanese for "moth-eaten" edges, are found on the ewer at many points on the hexagon shape.

2. Ewer
青花牛纹壶

Ming dynasty, ca. 1630–1645
Porcelain decorated in underglaze cobalt blue
H. 24.4 cm; W. 20.2 cm
Private Collection

This hexagonal ewer (Jp: *mizutsugi*) in the form of a kettle is reminiscent of Oribe ware ewers with loop handles (Jp: *suichu*), which are ultimately derived from Japanese metalwork.[1] It was probably made to hold water for replenishing the water jar in the latter part of the tea ceremony.[2] The ewer is decorated with the figures of eight water buffalo or oxen in various poses on the body and lid. One stares boldly out at the viewer, and another turns at an angle, its back and rump painted separately on the lid. The water buffalo, which have short horns, are outlined in broad brushstrokes of dark cobalt and infilled with graded washes to suggest three-dimensional form. Here, the potter-painter is probably the same man who

1. See Miyeko Murase, ed., *Turning Point: Oribe and the Arts of Sixteenth-Century Japan* (New York: Metropolitan Museum of Art, 2003), pp. 176–79, nos. 90–92.
2. Ibid., p. 177.
3. Awakawa Yasuichi, *Zen Painting: Brushmarks of Infinity* (Tokyo: Kodansha International, 1970), nos. 29, 75; Baird, *Symbols of Japan*, p. 154.

3. Fresh Water Jar

青花水族紋提梁水罐

Ming dynasty, ca. 1625–1635
Porcelain decorated in underglaze cobalt blue
H. 27.4 cm; Diam. 18.4 cm
Lent by the Asian Art Museum,
   Gift of Roy Leventritt (B69P95L)

This fresh-water jar (Jp: *mizusashi*) in the form of a wooden bucket is one of the more intriguing forms created by the potters of Jingdezhen for use in the Japanese tea ceremony. It was used to provide water for rinsing tea bowls and making tea. The sides are painted with panels resembling the staves of a bucket. Decorating the upper register as well as the flat lid are flying cranes, symbols of immortality often linked to Laozi, the great Daoist sage and immortal, alternating with conventional *ruyi* (Chinese for "wish-granting") clouds emitting extravagant tails and flourishes. The bottom register is painted with sea grasses and a variety of fish, including the common carp and mandarin fish, crabs, and shrimp. The handles of the bucket and the lid are painted with a border of meandering scrolls like those on the handle of the water jar decorated with water buffalo (cat. no. 2) and the peach-shaped ladle (cat. no. 1). At the top of the bucket handle is a motif often seen on exportwares of the 1630s and early 1640s, a peony blossom with lotus scrolls and tendrils. A raised band of clay encircling the body of the water jar mimics the iron band of a wooden bucket.

The water jar is heavily potted and its thick glaze of bluish tone is covered with numerous pinholes. There are countless *mushikui* on the edges of the handle and the lid, and on the band of clay around the center of the body. Kiln grit adheres in small clumps around the lower edge of the sides. The jar rests on a hastily beveled, undercut foot ring measuring 14.6 centimeters in diameter and almost 1.3 centimeters wide. Its unglazed bottom bears concentric circular rings which are evidence of finishing on the potter's wheel; there are also four slashes, probably from a finishing tool, and a small splash of clear glaze.

4. Water Jar

青花牡丹瑞兽纹水罐

Ming dynasty, ca. 1620–1630
Porcelain decorated in underglaze cobalt blue
H. 19 cm; Diam. 19.8 cm
Private Collection

This densely decorated water jar (Jp: *mizusashi*) was made to hold cold water for refilling the iron kettle used to make tea during the tea ceremony.[1] The decoration is very much in the style of Chinese export ware, particularly *kraak* ware made for the Dutch, Spanish, and Portuguese markets in the late Wanli period, around 1600 to 1620. Giant tree peonies, round buds, tendrils, and large, assertively veined leaves are set against a blue ground, consuming the sides of the jar. Four dogs of Fo, "Buddhistic" lion dogs, stand on long scrolling stalks of tree peony. These are imaginary lions, since they were not indigenous to China and Japan. Lions like these figure prominently in Buddhist imagery; they often guard sacred places, especially temples, and their roar represents "the voice of the law." In Japan, pairs of lions often guard the entrance to Shinto shrines as well. And lions and peony are associated in the Noh play *Shakkyo* [The Stone Bridge] about a pilgrimage to the Tiantai Mountains in southern China.[2]

The rim of the jar is densely decorated with a border of *ruyi*, "wish-granting," symbols and tendrils, while the underside of the rim is decorated with tendrils on a blue ground. Inside the body of the jar, a third rim is painted with two birds on rocks—one a duck and one known as a "wagtail" in Japan. Wagtails decorated Shino ware dishes of the Momoyama period (1573–1615).[3] Japanese potters must have borrowed the "wagtail" from some of the tens of thousands of kraak dishes known to this day as "the bird on the rock" in Holland. Some of these *kraak* dishes did find their way to Japan. The inner border is also embellished with rocks and bamboo, camellia, and an herbaceous peony.

The jar was raised on a wheel in two pieces, which were luted together although not thoroughly; the joint has fired a light orange in places where not entirely covered by the glaze. Its rim, which has an everted edge, appears to have been raised along with the upper half of the body. The glazed interior is covered with pinholes on the inside bottom. For such a large object, the jar is rather thinly potted. Its greyish body has fired orange in spots on the rim and above the foot where the glaze parted company with the body during firing. Five streaks or patches of glaze adhere to the otherwise unglazed bottom, which is very slightly undercut so that the jar actually rests on a foot ring about 0.8 cm wide. The foot ring is beveled on the outside. The jar has many *mushikui* and is quite warped. It has a lacquer lid which fits down into the body.

1. Murase, *Turning Point*, p. 123.
2. Baird, *Symbols of Japan*, p. 146.
3. See, for example, Murase, *Turning Point*, p. 80, no. 26.

5. Basket

青花山水葡萄纹提篮

Ming dynasty, ca. 1630–1645
Porcelain decorated in underglaze cobalt blue
H. 12.8 cm; W. 25.5 cm; D. 19.5 cm
Private Collection

This large, heavy *kosometsuke* basket was made for serving fish or other side dishes during the full tea ceremony. The form was based on early seventeenth-century Oribe ware in which handles were added to evoke the "basket work containers used in previous eras."[1] This basket was probably produced by the same kiln which made the small basket decorated with four horses (cat. no. 18); the melons, leaves, and tendrils decorating that basket are very similar to the grapes, leaves, and vines seen here. The landscape painted on the interior is very much in the tradition of Chinese scholars' paintings, and its style helps to date the basket. The composition is organized using horizontal elements of diminishing size to indicate recession. A lone scholar sits on a promontory overlooking the water; a flock of birds flies off into the distance above him. Two leafless trees and a pavilion share the foreground with the scholar. In the middle distance, a pavilion beneath a tree peers out from behind a small hill, and a single mountain peak looms in the far distance. The various elements of the scene are described by dark, imprecise outlines filled in with broad strokes of dark and medium wash. The grapes, leaves, and coiling vines which decorate the sides and handle are painted in the same manner.

This basket is very heavily potted and, like the smaller basket, is warped on the bottom and sides. The handle has vertical and horizontal firing cracks which reveal the way it was made: a long strip of clay was cut, two side pieces were added, and then the ends were luted onto the body of the basket. There are many *mushikui* on the basket's handle and rim. The unglazed bottom is finished with one bevel all the way around the edge. Pinholes fill the glaze over the landscape, and in many places small bits of glaze failed to adhere to the body, which has fired a bright orange.

1. Murase, *Turning Point*, p. 150.

6. Ewer
青花山水人物纹执壶
Ming dynasty, ca. 1635–1645
Porcelain decorated in underglaze cobalt blue
H. 14.9 cm; W. 22.9 cm
Private Collection

This ewer (Jp: *mizutsugi*) would have been used to add water to the water jar (Jp: *mizusashi*) during the latter part of the tea ceremony. The water jar was the source of water for the iron teakettle, which supplied hot water to wash out the tea bowls and to make the tea for the tea ceremony.[1] The ewer is decorated front and back with separate scenes set in a garden under clouds surrounding the roof of a heavenly palace and mountains. On one side, an adult scholar wearing a long robe and carrying a furled parasol turns to confront three boisterous boys, possibly future scholars; two are waving open fans, and one holds a folded fan in front of his legs. The scene to the right of the handle is very similar; all three boys are flourishing fans. In Chinese art, the subject of playing children was popular from the Southern Song dynasty (1127–1279) on and was particularly prevalent during the Ming. The swirling outlines of figures, landscape, and palace roofs effectively convey movement and energy to the ewer's surface.

The heavily-potted vessel was very rapidly produced. Its handle and spout do not line up evenly on opposite sides. Haphazardly applied, the glaze does not cover the lower body and is very unevenly applied on the inside near the rim. The unglazed bottom is trimmed with a single bevel around the outside. The unglazed lip at the mouth is broad and flat, indicating that the ewer would have had a lacquer or bronze lid when used in the tea ceremony.

1. Murase, *Turning Point*, pp. 177, 179.

39

7. Bowl
青花蓮口碗

Ming dynasty, ca. 1625–1635
Porcelain decorated in underglaze cobalt blue
H. 9.5 cm; Diam. 10.4 cm
Private Collection

This small, deep bowl (Jp: *mukozuke*) made in the form of a lotus was used to serve food during the *kaiseki*, the formal meal of the Japanese tea ceremony. Its shape is indirectly related to Oribe ware *mukozuke*, which were sometimes modeled in the form of the chrysanthemum.[1] Like the Oribe chrysanthemum-shaped *mukozuke*, this bowl was probably formed on a mold placed on a potter's wheel.

The bowl is decorated with a variety of flowers and symbols which have connotations in Buddhist, Daoist, and Chinese folk beliefs. Among the symbols decorating the large petals around the center are a Buddhist conch shell and, proceeding to the right, a folding fan, which in the older flat, rigid form was an attribute of Zhongli Quan, leader of the Eight Daoist Immortals.[2] Next is the artemisia leaf, one of the Eight Precious Symbols in China. The barrel drum is associated with the thunder god in Japan and with the Duke of Thunder, a Daoist deity, in China.[3] The stone chimes are another of the Eight Precious Symbols, as are the two books, represented as blue rectangles tied together in the middle with a string. At the top of the bowl, the petals are painted with flowers and fruit also freighted with messages: the lotus, a Buddhist symbol of purity; the Daoist peach of immortality; the tree peony, "flower of wealth and rank" or "king of flowers" in China; the camellia, a symbol of spring; the prunus, or plum, another symbol of spring; and finally, the chrysanthemum, a symbol of autumn and an allusion to Tao Qian (Tao Yuanming; 365–427), a famous Chinese poet-recluse.[4] Swastikas, an auspicious Buddhist symbol, are painted just below the rim.

The bowl is crudely potted. Its glazed interior is decorated with an outlined peony or cherry blossom and has three large firing cracks where the bottom meets the sides. On the exterior, at the joint above the foot ring, the glaze has pulled away from the body during firing to reveal a very orange body. Above the foot, the glaze has pooled and turned a deep green. The bowl has a number of bubbles, firing flaws, and cracks on the outside. Its lively blue cobalt pigment has fired blue-black at the tops of the peach and peony. The shallow foot ring is undercut and unbeveled, smoothed only with a tool. The glazed bottom is marked with four thunderbolt symbols (Jp: raimon; Ch: leiwen) enclosed in a square.[5]

1. Murase, *Turning Point*, p. 169, no. 85.
2. The folding fan was invented in Japan but became very popular in China during the Ming dynasty.
3. Stephen Little with Shawn Eichman, *Taoism and the Arts of China* (Chicago: Art Institute of Chicago, 2000), pp. 238–39; Baird, *Symbols of Japan*, p. 283.
4. Terese Tse Bartholomew, "Botanical Motifs in Chinese Furniture," *Journal of the Classical Chinese Furniture Society* 2, no. 4 (Autumn 1992), pp. 39, 41, 45, and 46–47.
5. Baird, *Symbols of Japan*, p. 39.

8. Two Dishes
青花相扑纹圆盘

Ming dynasty, ca. 1625–1635
Porcelain decorated in underglaze cobalt blue
H. 2.5 cm; Diam. 15.2 cm
H. 2.7 cm; Diam. 15.2 cm
Lent by the Asian Art Museum; Effie B. Allison Collection, Gift of J.V. West and B.V. Gewald (B81P35, B81P36)

These small dishes, probably part of a set of five made for the Japanese market, express the humor and vigor of early *kosometsuke* wares. Each dish depicts two pugilists in different postures. One pair is caught in the stylized poses appropriate to the beginning of combat; the second pair is engaged in judo-like maneuvers, striking with their legs and arms or fending off their opponent's blows. The ground plane is shared by a pine with weirdly contorted trunk and three bizarre clumps of needles which loom over the combatants. On the left, a clothes rack holds a garment. Wispy clouds and a small sun complete the scene. All this is painted with a few sure strokes; there are no graded washes. The fighters' stances, the left leaning pine, and the clouds provide a sense of movement to the scene.

The dishes are sturdily potted of poorly levigated clay, which has caused many pinholes to pop through the thick greyish glaze. They are painted with a poor quality dark cobalt pigment. Kiln grit adheres to the front of the dishes as well as to the foot ring. Chatter marks are visible through the glaze on the bottom, and on both dishes, the glaze has pulled away from the foot ring to reveal unusually orange bodies. Both dishes have many sizable *mushikui*. Each foot ring is decorated on the outside by two blue bands, and a single line encircles each dish under the everted rim. Four pearls, each surrounded with four dots, decorate the backs of the dishes.

9. Dish

青花富士山形盘

Ming dynasty, ca. 1625–1635
Porcelain decorated in underglaze cobalt blue
H. 6. 4 cm; W. 27.9 cm; D. 24.8 cm
Lent by the Asian Art Museum,
    Gift of Roy Leventritt (B69P98L)

This dish was made for service in the tea ceremony. Its form derives from the Japanese lacquer tray and more immediately from the Oribe stoneware dishes made in the late sixteenth and early seventeenth centuries in Japan. The triangular dish, with three lobes separated by ridges at the top, echoes the shape of Mount Fuji, Japan's most sacred mountain and, as such, a major pilgrimage site throughout history.[1] Like China, Japan has a long tradition of venerating the mountain. From earliest times, mountains provided a conduit between heaven and earth for gods and spirits. Shinto, Japan's earliest religion, which persists today, is based directly on nature; exceptional rocks and rocky places, regarded as a manifestation of the creative life force of the universe, have been designated sacred sites. Buddhists built their monasteries in the mountainous wilderness to obtain the peace necessary for meditation. Daoists shared with Buddhists the ideal of withdrawal to mountains and caves for self-cultivation and, in the case of the Daoists, for the performance of rituals and alchemy.[2]

This dish is decorated with a landscape composed with a series of receding ground planes. In the foreground, deer and horses cavort across rocky promontories; a willow stands behind the two horses. In the middle ground, mountains are stacked one beside another in a manner reminiscent of earlier landscape conventions; the individual peaks are formed of contours repeated one atop the other to suggest mass. A leafless tree clings to a peak in the middle ground, and above it stands a tree with tiny blossoms, a prunus, significant for blooming earlier than other trees. In the far distance, an eight-character inscription beside three flying birds hangs beneath horizontal clouds. The inscription reads *mu shi yu ju, lu ma yu you*: "living among trees and rocks, roaming with deer and horse." The sides of the dish are decorated with a basket weave border.

The base was made from a large slab of clay; its sides, made from long, narrow strips, were luted onto the base. Three U-shaped feet created from strips of clay are attached to the bottom at each corner and then squared

off. This method of construction mimics that of Oribe wares. The dish is painted with a very good quality blue cobalt, far better than the cobalt used on most *kosometsuke* wares, which leads one to date the dish to the 1630s. Good quality cobalt was more readily available at that time than in the Tianqi era (1621–1627). This dish was probably made at the same workshop as the two gourd-shaped dishes in the exhibition (cat. nos. 10, 21), with which it shares potting characteristics.[3] But unlike the gourd-shaped dishes, the base does not ripple. There are numerous *mushikui* on its rim, particularly along the left ridge that intersects the clouds. A glaze of blue-green tone covers all but the bottoms of the U-shaped feet.

1. Kawahara Masahiko, *Ko-sometsuke*, vol. 2, *Monochrome Section* (Kyoto: Kyoto Shoin, 1977), plates 294, 295.
2. Baird, *Symbols of Japan*, pp. 33–36.
3. Stephen Little, "Ko-sometsuke in the Asian Art Museum of San Francisco," *Orientations* 13 (April 1982), p. 18. I am indebted to Little for the translation of the inscription.

10. Dish

青花山水人物紋瓠形盤

Ming dynasty, ca. 1625–1635
Porcelain decorated in underglaze cobalt blue
H. 6.4 cm; W. 24.1 cm; D. 19.7 cm
Lent by the Asian Art Museum,
    Gift of Roy Leventritt (B69P97L)

This gourd-shaped dish was made specifically for serving food during the *kaiseki*, the small meal in the tea ceremony. Its form is ultimately related to the simple lacquer trays popular in Japan. It was made in the same way as many Oribe dishes: a rolled slab of clay was cut to the desired shape to form the base, and long thin slabs of clay were luted onto the base to form the sides. The three feet were each created from a rolled tube bent into a U-shape, fastened at both ends to the base, and smoothed on the bottom with a knife.

The dish is decorated with the figure of a scholar on horseback preceded by three servants carrying his possessions, including a *qin*, or Chinese zither. The ability to play the *qin* represented one of the four scholarly accomplishments. Another servant carries a parasol, which signified the scholar's status as one who had passed the imperial civil service examinations. The group proceeds through a mountainous landscape. As on the Mount Fuji-shaped dish (cat. no. 9), the contours of the distant mountains are repeated side by side or on top of one another in a manner reminiscent of earlier landscapes on porcelain. Six birds fly across the sky. A most unusual border decorates the outside of the dish. It consists of larger and smaller blue rondels—which Terese Bartholomew has characterized as "wish-granting pearls,"[1] some connected to long tail-like streaks as if floating on water.

Its potting characteristics are similar to those of the Mount Fuji-shaped dish (cat. no. 9) and the gourd-

shaped dish decorated with the dragon, monkey, and peach tree (cat. no. 21). The interior and bottom surfaces are quite wavy, reflecting the haste with which the dish was produced. It is painted in a cobalt blue of good quality; the thick glaze is blue-green and has a number of sizable pinholes. The rim is painted under the glaze with a pale blue wash but large patches of glaze with bits of the blue trim have flaked off after firing, leaving numerous *mushikui*. Kiln grit adheres to the glazed bottom, and the glaze has fallen away at the juncture between bottom and sides, leaving long strips of *mushikui*. The bottoms of the feet are unglazed.

1. Personal communication with Terese Bartholomew, Asian Art Museum of San Francisco.

11. Incense Box
青花方形香盒
Ming dynasty, ca. 1620–1630
Porcelain decorated in underglaze cobalt blue
H. 4.7 cm; W. 5.4 cm; D. 4.1 cm
Lent by the Asian Art Museum,
    Gift of Roy Leventritt (B69P96L a.-b.)

This small incense box (Jp: *kōgō*) was made for the Japanese market early in the period of increased trade with Japan, after the closure of the imperial kilns in Jingdezhen. Like a few other porcelains in the exhibition, the decoration reflects conventions of the Wanli era (1573–1620). The lid on the rectangular box is decorated with a sleeping water buffalo modeled in high relief and surrounded on all four sides by painted clouds shaped like the Chinese *ruyi*, "wish-granting," symbol. The long sides of the box are each painted with a pair of books representing scholarship, one of the Eight Precious Symbols. The short ends are painted with cymbidium orchids, symbolic of the reclusive scholar, because the small flower reveals its presence in the grass with subtle scent rather than with gaudy blossoms. Such auspicious motifs as *ruyi*-shaped clouds, pairs of books, cymbidiums, and long grasses—all painted in great haste with dark cobalt—are found on late Wanli and Tianqi domestic porcelains and on export wares for all markets.

The little box evinces classic potting characteristics of early *kosometsuke*. It is sturdily potted, sits on four stubby feet, and is covered with a thick blue-green glaze. The back and neck of the water buffalo are covered with

mushikui, as are the front of the lid and the edges around the bottom. On the bottom, the thick glaze has pulled away, exposing the body, which with its high iron content has fired a bright orange. Kiln grit adheres to the bottom of all four unglazed feet.

12. Incense Container
青花鵪鶉形香盒
Ming dynasty, ca. 1630–1645
Porcelain decorated in underglaze cobalt blue
H. 3.8 cm; W. 5.6 cm; D. 3.5 cm
Lent by the Asian Art Museum; Effie B. Allison
    Collection, Gift of J.V. West and B.V. Gewald
    (B81P49 a.-b.)

This tiny box in the form of a quail was made to hold small bits of incense to be added to the charcoal before the host made tea during the tea ceremony. If this part of the ritual were omitted, the *kōgō* could have been placed in the alcove (Jp: *tokonoma*) of the tea room for the guests to inspect and admire.[1] So valued were these objects to tea people (Jp: *chajin*) that a list of Japan's greatest *kōgō* was drawn up in the mid-nineteenth century. This particular *kōgō* was reputed to have belonged to the tea master Fujimura Shoin (1650–1733).[2]

Known for its pugnacious nature, the quail symbolizes courage in Japan as well as in China. It was also a symbol of autumn and, because of its drab coloration, of

poverty.[3] The Chinese word for "quail," *an*, is a homophone for the word meaning "peace." Because of its association with autumn, the quail was portrayed with stalks of grain in seventeenth-century Japan and China. In China, the quail and grain (*sui*) evoked the wish *suisui ping'an*, "peace year after year."[4] This *kōgō* is skillfully painted with different strokes to indicate the difference in texture of the bird's back and breast feathers and its wings. The inside is glazed, top and bottom; the unglazed bottom bears a firing crack.

1. Murase, *Turning Point*, p. 140.
2. Yoshiko Kakudo, *The Effie B. Allison Collection: Kosometsuke and Other Chinese Blue-and-White Porcelains* (San Francisco: Asian Art Museum, 1982), pp. 5, 13.
3. Baird, *Symbols of Japan*, p. 118.
4. Terese Tse Bartholomew, "Imperial Rebuses at the Qing Court," *Society of Asian Art Newsletter* 36, no. 1 (Fall, 1996), p. 5.

13. Seal Paste Box
青花圓形印泥盒
Ming dynasty, ca. 1635–1645
Porcelain decorated in underglaze cobalt blue
H. 4.8 cm; Diam. 6.2 cm
Lent by the Asian Art Museum; Effie B. Allison
    Collection, Gift of J.V. West and B.V. Gewald
    (B81P29 a.-b.)

This small seal paste box is the only porcelain in the exhibition that was not made expressly for the Japanese market. For many centuries, Japanese tea connoisseurs adapted and treasured objects made for the Chinese by Chinese potters. Longquan celadons, Jian ware hare's fur tea bowls, and early Ming blue-and-

white wares are only the most familiar of these objects.[1] This small box, purchased in Japan by an American collector, was adapted for use as an incense container (*kōgō*) in the formal tea ceremony. It was in fact originally made to hold seal paste for literate Chinese; this type was also exported to overseas Chinese communities throughout Southeast Asia. There were many, many similar seal paste boxes in a variety of sizes in the "Hatcher Cargo," salvaged from a ship sunk soon after 1643 in the South China Sea and sold at Christie's, Amsterdam, in March and June of 1984. Only those with the most spectacular decoration were illustrated,[2] and the Hatcher Cargo catalogues make no mention of seal paste boxes decorated with a figure of a horse. But its potting characteristics make the container's origins plain. The body and glaze are quite white in comparison to *kosometsuke* wares, and the cobalt blue is more vivid than the blue-black of many of the examples in the exhibition. The box is decorated with a band of *ruyi*-shaped clouds rendered in dark wash which alternate with light blue wispy clouds. A firing crack mars the horse's belly.

1. See Seizo Hayashiya and Henry Trubner, et al., *Chinese Ceramics from Japanese Collections: T'ang through Ming Dynasties* (New York: Asia Society and John Weatherhill, 1977), nos. 20, 22, 24, 33, 34, 45, 46.
2. See, for example, Colin Sheaf and Richard Kilburn, *The Hatcher Porcelain Cargoes: the Complete Record* (Oxford: Phaidon, 1988), plates 83 and 84.

14. Incense Container
青花螺形香盒

Ming dynasty, ca. 1625–1640
Porcelain decorated in underglaze cobalt blue
H. 4.2 cm; Diam. 3.6 cm
Lent by the Asian Art Museum; Effie B. Allison
    Collection, Gift of J.V. West and B.V. Gewald
    (B81P50 a.-b.)

The incense container (Jp: *kōgō*) was produced in Jingdezhen solely for the Japanese market. Like their Japanese predecessors in Oribe ware, Chinese porcelain *kōgō* were made in a myriad forms representing animate and inanimate subjects. Numerous examples are illustrated in Kawahara's *Ko-sometsuke*.[1] But because they are so highly prized to this day, they are seldom seen in the West. Incense containers in the shape of a snail come in two forms, an upright snail (Jp: *tachibai*) like this *kōgō* and a recumbent snail (Jp: *yokobai*). The specific nomenclature attached to particular forms of *kōgō* is an indication of the reverence with which Japanese tea masters regarded these small containers.

The top and bottom were molded separately; both were painted in dark cobalt and sprayed lightly with cobalt pigment blown through a bamboo tube with gauze at one end to produce an effect known in Japanese as *fukizumi*, "blown ink." The inside is glazed, while the flat, unglazed bottom has fired a brilliant orange, as has a small indentation on the rim and the join between top and bottom.

1. Kawahara, *Ko-sometsuke*, vol. 2, Monochrome Section, nos. 1–115.

46

15. Incense Container

青花方形香盒

Ming dynasty, ca. 1630–1640
Porcelain decorated in underglaze cobalt blue
H. 6.5 cm; W. 4 cm
Peggy and Richard M. Danziger Collection

Incense boxes are among the most treasured of all tea paraphernalia. According to Louise Cort, this sophisticated square incense container is made in the shape of a bridge pile (Jp: *hashigui*), one of the nineteen shapes of incense containers classified by Japanese connoisseurs.[1]

This particular *kōgō* is very carefully potted and painted. The sides of the container are subtly chamfered, and the upper edge of the top is beveled on all four sides. Decorating the upper surface of the top as well as the separate sides of the top and bottom are different finely painted diaper patterns like those on numerous other porcelains in this catalogue and on *kraak* dishes made for the European and Middle Eastern markets between about 1600 and 1645. The glaze on the interior has a few pinholes, and the inside of the lid has a firing crack. Two corners of the bottom and the sides and top have small *mushikui*. The rim of the bottom is unglazed, as is the bottom of the container.

1. Personal communication with Louise Cort, Curator for Ceramics at the Freer Gallery of Art and Arthur M. Sackler Gallery, Washington, D.C.

16. Charcoal Container

青花炭罐

Ming dynasty, ca. 1630–1645
Porcelain decorated in underglaze cobalt blue
H. 10.4 cm; W. 9.5 cm
Private Collection

This small square container was made to sit on a tobacco tray (Jp: *tabako-bon*). Tobacco became available in Japan by the early seventeenth century, and tea masters provided guests with tobacco trays bearing pipes, tongs, a container of loose tobacco, and a jar for ash refuse to be used in their waiting rooms before the tea ceremony. The charcoal container was filled with ash and a piece of charcoal placed on the ash. Guests would pick up the charcoal with tongs to light their pipes.[1]

All four sides of this charcoal container are decorated with a single continuous scene. A junk with its sail furled is being pulled through choppy waters by three men in harness. The boat's square bow continues around the corner of the container, following behind a harnessed man who has just traversed rocky, difficult terrain. Two other harnessed men continue around the container's third side and are about to confront a rocky promontory with a stunted tree growing out over the water. The boat's stern completes the scene. On the container's fourth side, a pilot holding the tiller with intense concentration begins the

narrative again. Much of the decoration is painted in outline, notably the figures and the waves which are rendered in a stylized pattern known as *araumi*, "rough seas," in Japan.[2] A scroll border decorates the container's square foot. The thick glaze has many dark pinholes and has flaked off extensively on the corners of the container; the rim has many *mushikui*. The square foot ring is warped, beveled, and undercut and has two vertical firing cracks in one corner. The bottom is glazed and bears a four-character mark reading *da ming nian zhi*, "made in the reign of the great Ming," in regular script.

1. Sōshitsu Sen XV, ed., *Chanoyu: the Urasenke Tradition of Tea*, trans. Alfred Birnbaum (New York and Tokyo: Weatherhill, 1988), p. 57. See also Sen'ō Tanaka and Sendō Tanaka, *The Tea Ceremony*, rev. ed. (Tokyo, New York; London, Kodansha International, 2000), p. 171; a tobacco tray is illustrated at the top of the page.
2. Baird, *Symbols of Japan*, p. 43.

17. Water Jar
青花八骏图盖罐
Ming dynasty, ca. 1620–1630
Porcelain decorated in underglaze cobalt blue
H. 15 cm; Diam. 21 cm (rim); Diam. 18 (base)
Peggy and Richard M. Danziger Collection

This cylindrical water jar (Jp: *mizusashi*) is a rare survival of the Tianqi era; its top and bottom are both in mint condition. The *mizusashi* is the largest ceramic utensil used in the formal tea ceremony; it holds the water with which

the iron teakettle is refilled during the tea ceremony. The hot water from the iron kettle is then used to warm the tea bowls and make tea.[1]

The lid is concave and has a lug handle with two sizable *mushikui* on it. A landscape painted in broad brush strokes decorates the lid. The body has an inverted rim decorated with a border of blossoms and tendrils. Painted on the sides of the jar are seven horses, two of them piebald, covered in large dark spots placed with little concern for the horses' anatomy. Three of the horses are lying down; one rolls on his back with his legs in the air, and another gallops through the abstract landscape, mane and tail flying. The landscape is depicted with tufts of long grass and abstract clouds.

The horses on the jar may have represented seven of the eight horses of King Mu to the potter-painters of Jingdezhen. King Mu (10th c. BCE), the fifth Zhou dynasty emperor, possessed mythic powers and drove a chariot pulled by eight horses, each with a different supernatural attribute. For instance, Beyond Earth had hooves that did not touch the ground, and Faster than Shadow could move with the sun.[2] King Mu's horses were depicted in paintings and the decorative arts from the Tang dynasty (618–906) on. But the horse also had special meaning for the Japanese. The Shinto religion posited horses as regulators of rainfall and messengers between earth and the heavens. White horses were kept at Shinto shrines but this soon proved impractical, so large sculptures were substituted. The horse is the mount of the Buddhist deity Nichiten, god of the sun. And in Japanese folk religion, the horse was painted on votive plaques known as *ema*, "picture horses," which were placed at shrines and temples to carry peoples' prayers to the dieties.[3]

The body of the water jar was thrown in two parts and luted together. It is heavily potted of relatively well-levigated clay but has many pinholes in the glaze, including a line of pinholes above the wispy clouds depicted on the sides. The jar and lid are painted with bright cobalt and covered with a thick glaze of bluish cast; specks of cobalt are visible on the jar's white ground. Chatter marks are visible two-thirds of the way around the base, which has been finished with a rag and a tool; large black bits of kiln grit have stuck to the base. The underside of the lid is glazed and has numerous pinholes. The interior of the jar is glazed except on the bottom.

1. Murase, *Turning Point*, p. 123
2. Anne Birrell, *Chinese Mythology: An Introduction* (Baltimore and London: Johns Hopkins University Press, 1993), pp. 236–37.
3. Baird, *Symbols of Japan*, pp. 143–44.

18. Basket

青花骏马图提篮

Ming dynasty, ca. 1630–1645
Porcelain decorated in underglaze cobalt blue
H. 11.5 cm; W. 17.8 cm; D. 14.5 cm
Private Collection

Like the previous basket (cat. no. 5), this heavy container was based on an Oribe ware prototype and might have been used to serve small bits of fish or other side dishes to guests taking part in the meal, *kaiseki,* served during the tea ceremony.[1] The horses which decorate this basket may represent four of the eight horse of King Mu (10th c. BCE), each of which had a specific name and association with mythical powers: Windswept Plumes, for example, was faster than a winged bird, and Finer-than- Flashing-Light had a coat of dazzling light. The horses enabled King Mu to tour his empire in a chariot as swift as a dragon and to visit Xiwangmu, Queen Mother of the West, in her celestial territory in western China.[2] The horse on the upper left strides like a dressage horse practicing the Passage movement; the horse on the right kicks up his heels. On the lower right, a third horse trots towards the fourth horse which is lying down. Three small clumps of grass indicate the horses' field, and a horizontal cloud completes the scene. The handle of the basket is decorated with a prunus blossom with leaves and tendrils. Two melons with large leaves and trailing vines are painted on the sides at the narrow ends of the basket, while a flaming cloud decorates the center of each side beneath the handle.

The basket is very heavily potted of poorly levigated clay and covered with a glaze of grey-blue tone. Inside the basket, the glaze did not completely cover the sides; long streaks of the exposed body have fired a light orange. The unglazed bottom is warped; it was finished with a tool and wiped with a rag. Bits of kiln grit adhere to the inside and on the bottom, both of which are full of pinholes. There are three small firing cracks where the handle joins the sides of the basket.

1. Murase, *Turning Point*, p. 150, no 69.
2. Birrell, *Chinese Mythology*, pp. 173, 236–37.

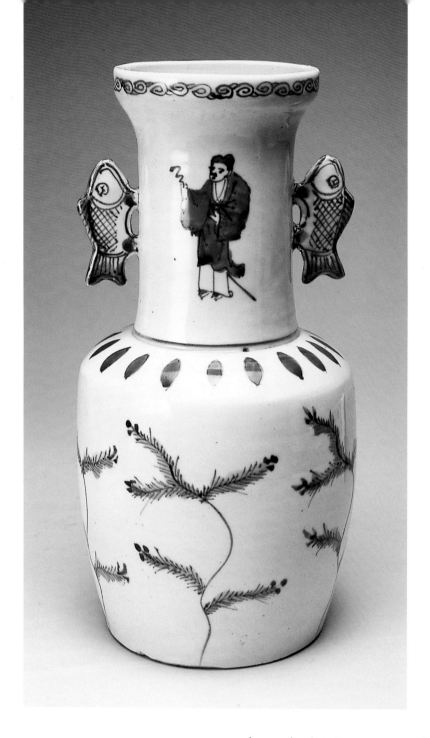

19. Vase

青花鱼耳瓶

Possibly 18th-century Japanese copy

Porcelain decorated in underglaze cobalt blue

H. 28.8 cm; Diam. 14.2 cm

Lent by the Asian Art Museum; Effie B. Allison
    Collection, Gift of J.V. West and B.V. Gewald
    (B81P2)

This vase is one of a group made for use in the alcove, or *tokonoma*, of a teahouse or in a more informal setting. The form is inspired by the Longquan celadon vases with fish or dragon handles of the Southern Song dynasty (1127–1279). Highly prized in Japan, these celadon vases

are known by their Japanese name, *kinuta*, because they are shaped like the mallet used to pound and soften bolts of silk before cutting and sewing. Blue-and-white vases of this shape are referred to in Japan as "Takasago" vases. They are usually decorated with male and female figures which recall Jo and Uba, a spirit couple who rake sand and sweep the pine groves at Takasago on the Inland Sea. Their images symbolize longevity and marital fidelity in Japan. Jo and Uba are the principal characters in the Noh play *Takasago*, and their representation on this type of vase, according to Henry Trubner, bespeaks the connection between the choreography and philosophy of the Noh theater and the "stylized movements, formal dress and spiritual mood that became essential components of the fully developed tea ceremony."[1] So popular were these Takasago vases among tea enthusiasts that, according to Kawahara Masahiko, the vases were soon copied in Japan, especially in Kyoto; famous potters have left documentation detailing the method of creating *mushikui*, "moth-eaten" edges, on the later copies.[2]

The vase in the Allison Collection differs in several respects from other wares in the exhibition and from similar vases pictured in Kawahara's *Ko-sometsuke*.[3] Its neck is decorated on either side with a hermit sage holding a staff, whereas those published by Kawahara are decorated on one side of the neck with a male figure wearing a hat and on the other with a female figure holding a staff. The Allison vase is heavier and has a thicker neck than the much more attenuated vases illustrated by Kawahara or Hayashiya and Trubner.[4] It is covered with a heavy glaze of bluish-green cast which is markedly dull and flat compared to the Japanese-market wares in the Asian Art Museum's collections. These differences in proportions and glaze quality suggested to Yoshiko Kakudo that the Allison vase might be a later copy.[5] Several other anomalies characterize the vase. The scroll border around the neck is mechanically drawn, while the grid decorating the bodies of the fish handles is awkwardly spaced and painted in a heavy-handed manner. The washes of blue pigment in the petals on the shoulder are not all applied vertically; some are applied horizontally, some crosswise. Inside the neck of the vase, an unglazed patch of the body has fired two different colors; unglazed bodies of Japanese-market wares generally fire a uniform color. The unglazed foot ring has fired a light orange, and a large amorphous patch of yellowish kiln sand and grit adorns the glazed bottom. Both the color of the foot and the color of the kiln sand and grit differ from those of other wares in the exhibition. These subtle differences seem to indicate that the Allison vase is a later copy, possibly Japanese, of a Ming dynasty "Takasago" vase made at Jingdezhen between 1625 and 1645. It is included in the exhibition because it illustrates the form of one of Japan's most popular vases used in the alcove, or *tokonoma*, of a teahouse

1. Hayashiya and Trubner, *Chinese Ceramics from Japanese Collections*, p. 109.
2. In Kakudo, *The Effie B. Allison Collection*, p. 11.
3. Kawahara, *Ko-sometsuke*, vol. 2, *Monochrome Section*, pp. 35–36.
4. The vase illustrated in Hayashiya and Trubner, no. 62, is the same vase illustrated in Kawahara, *Ko-sometsuke*, vol. 2, *Monochrome Section*, p. 36, no. 132.
5. Kakudo, *The Effie B. Allison Collection*, p. 11.

20. Plate

青花山水人物纹圆盘
Ming dynasty, ca. 1625–1635
Porcelain decorated in underglaze cobalt blue
H. 2.6 cm; Diam. 21 cm
Lent by the Asian Art Museum,
    Gift of Roy Leventritt (B69P87L)

With its grey-greenish glaze, heavy potting, poorly levigated body, and broad-brush painting in blue-black cobalt pigment, this heavy plate on a wide foot ring is a quintessential example of *kosometsuke* ware. The plate is decorated with the figure of a woman riding through a landscape rendered in conventions typical of the 1610s and 1620s. She rides across what is essentially a bumpy ground line, part of which turns precipitously upward. At the right stands a tall pine depicted with contorted trunk, clusters of needles, and trailing vines. The pine's highest branch seems to merge into the same plane occupied by distant mountains and a sun, about to disappear under a cloud. Because the lady is riding an elegantly caparisoned horse and holding a triangular banner, she may represent Lady Wang Zhaojun or Lady Wenji, both women of the Han dynasty (206 BCE–220 CE) who were married to Xiongnu tribesmen. Lady Wang was sent by the emperor to improve relations with the non-Chinese peoples on the northern frontier; she sacrificed her personal wishes for the good of her country. Lady Wenji was kidnapped. After twelve years in the north, she was found

and ransomed, but had to abandon her two sons and their "barbarian" father to return to her native China. At the request of the late Han statesman Cao Cao, Wenji transcribed from memory some of the lost works of her father, the famous Confucian scholar Cai Yong (132–192), who had died tragically in prison. Thus Lady Wenji, a talented musician, scholar, and poetess, became an eternal symbol of the proper commitment to Confucian values, particularly filial piety, and the superiority of the Chinese way of life.

The plate is very heavily potted of badly levigated clay and has a thick upturned rim with a large firing crack. Numerous dark pinholes mar the front and back of the dish. The heavy foot ring is shallow and beveled. Brown kiln grit adheres to the glaze on the underside of more than half the foot ring as well as to the foot, which is decorated on the outside with two blue lines. The glazed bottom bears an apocryphal six-character Chenghua (1465–1487) reign mark in underglaze blue surrounded by a single blue line.

21. Dish

青花瓠形盘

Ming dynasty, ca. 1625–1635
Porcelain decorated in underglaze cobalt blue
H. 6.7 cm; W. 26 cm; D. 20.6 cm
Lent by the Asian Art Museum,
    Gift of Roy Leventritt (B69P99L)

This trefoil dish is described as gourd-shaped by Kawahara Masahiko.[1] The shape of the dish may be related to the story depicted on it. A sly monkey stands next to a peach tree, and a dragon emerges from the clouds above a clump of bamboo. The monkey probably represents Sun Wukong (Sun Houzi), the monkey king who became the central character of the late Ming novel *Xiyou ji* [Journey to the West]; set in the Tang dynasty (618–906), it is one of China's great tales of the supernatural as well as of the martial arts. The novel recounts Monkey's journey from China to India and back with a monk and other unusual companions to bring the complete Buddhist scriptures back to China. But long before the monkey king redeemed himself on this epic journey, he was known as a heavenly troublemaker. His principal transgression was stealing and eating the peaches of immortality that he was supposed to be superintending. The wrathful dragon on the dish could represent Aoguang Longwang, the Dragon King of the Eastern Sea, from whom Monkey procured his magic wand, or perhaps Huangdi, Lord of Heaven and Earth, who was almost perennially displeased with Monkey until his redemptive journey. After stealing and eating the peaches of immortality, Monkey stole and ate the pills of immortality which Laozi kept in five gourds in his heavenly palace.[2] This might account for the gourd-like shape of the dish. Outside the rim of the dish is a border of blue lozenges with white leaves in reserve. An eight-character poem which hangs above the peach tree reads *fei long zai tian, hua yuan yu tao*: "Flying dragon in the sky transforms the monkey near the peach tree."[3] Three different trefoil dishes with this decorative motif are pictured in Kawahara's *Ko-sometsuke*;[4] no other trifoliate dishes, large or small, appear in any of the literature on *kosometsuke*.

The dish shares potting characteristics with the other two large dishes from the Leventritt Collection (cat. nos. 9, 10), although the cobalt on this dish did not fire to as brilliant a blue as on the other two. The light-blue glazed rim has many *mushikui*, as has the joint between the sides and the rim. The interior and bottom of the dish, formed from a slab of clay, are wavy. Its three U-shaped feet are cut flat and left unglazed on their bottoms.

1. Kawahara, *Ko-sometsuke*; vol. 1, *Color Section*, pp. 90–91, plates 73, 74.
2. For a concise account of the monkey king, see E.T. Chalmers Werner, *Myths and Legends of China* (New York: Brentano's, 1922), pp. 325–69.
3. Little, "*Ko-sometsuke*," p. 18. I am indebted to Stephen Little for this translation.
4. Kawahara, *Ko-sometsuke*, vol. 2, *Monochrome Section*, pp. 66, 67.

22. Five Dishes

青花瓜瓞纹套盘

Ming dynasty, ca. 1625–1635
Porcelain decorated in underglaze cobalt blue
H. 3.8 cm; W. 14.9 cm
Lent by the Asian Art Museum; Effie B. Allison Collection, Gift of J.V. West and B.V. Gewald (B81P17–21)

This set of five dishes (Jp: *mukozuke*) was used for serving food during the *kaiseki*, a meal which preceded the serving of thick tea (Jp: *koicha*) during the tea ceremony. The dishes are made in the shape of a variety of melon popu-

lar in Japan and known there as *akadouri*. A squirrel sits nibbling on top of one of the two melons depicted in the center of each dish. Hastily drawn leaves and wiry vines fill most of the surface of each dish; these curling vines can be seen on other wares in the exhibition, including the rim of a deep dish decorated with a landscape (cat. no. 81). The painting of the vines is graphic testimony to the speed with which the wares of the period were decorated using the dark cobalt pigment. The dishes are covered with a thick glaze of bluish-grey cast which has flaked off during the firing in places to reveal an orange body; there are numerous *mushikui* on the rims of the dishes. Each dish sits upon four stubby feet, unglazed at the bottoms.

23. Bowl
青花牛纹碗
Ming dynasty, ca. 1625–1640
Porcelain decorated in underglaze cobalt blue
H. 7.9 cm; W. 10.8 cm
Lent by the Asian Art Museum; Effie B. Allison
    Collection, Gift of J.V. West and B.V. Gewald
    (B81P28)

This small bowl is decorated with the figures of eight water buffalo, or oxen, painted by the same hand that painted the water jar in the shape of a kettle (cat. no. 2). Reflecting the potter-painter's sense of humor, an ox gazes directly out at the viewer from the surface of the pot. The forms of the oxen are outlined with parallel brush strokes

of dark cobalt blue and filled in with a lighter wash to convey the solidity of their bodies. Each is portrayed from a different angle. In China, the ox is associated with the Daoist philosopher Laozi, who is said to have passed into immortality riding on an ox. The *Ten Oxherding Songs* (Ch: *Shiniu tu song*), parables identified with Chan Buddhism, originated in Song dynasty China and became popular in Japan; in this cycle of poems, the herdboy attains enlightenment while looking for his lost ox. In Japan, the ninth-century aristocrat Tenjin was deified as the god of calligraphy and is associated with the ox and the prunus. But most pervasive in Japan was the use of the ox as a talisman; it was believed that the ox could ward off smallpox.[1]

The bowl is not circular; the potter elongated the body and rim to a point on one side. It was probably one of a set of mukozuke dishes and used to serve food rather than drink. The vessel is sturdily potted and covered with a thick bluish-white glaze; there are numerous pinholes on the exterior, interior, and glazed bottom. Its unglazed foot is round and quite thick, and there is a firing crack running through it. Large chunks of kiln grit are stuck to the glaze inside the foot.

1. Baird, *Symbols of Japan*, pp. 154–56.

24. Dish
青花鱼形盘
Ming dynasty, ca. 1625–1635
Porcelain decorated in underglaze cobalt blue
H. 3 cm; W. 21.2 cm; D. 8.5 cm
Butler Family Collection

This footed dish in the form of a fish is probably the common carp (*Cyprinus carpio carpio*), *li yu* in Chinese. It was part of a set of five or ten dishes used for the *kaiseki*, the formal meal which accompanies a tea gathering. In the Tianqi and Chongzhen eras (1621–1644), footed dishes in the form of birds, beasts, and comestibles were made only for the Japanese market.

Fish were one of the most frequently depicted of all motifs used in Chinese art. A Daoist symbol of freedom from worldly restraint, it is the subject of one of Daoism's most famous stories. In a chapter of *Zhuangzi* entitled "Autumn Floods," Zhuangzi debated the Confucian Huizi on the banks of the Hao River. Huizi challenged Zhuangzi's ability to know what gives fish pleasure; since Zhuangzi is not a fish, how can he know what fish enjoy? Zhuangzi

replied that he knows intuitively by watching the fish in the very river they sat beside—the intuitive triumphed over the logical.[1] The Chinese word for "fish," *yu*, is a homophone for the word meaning "abundance." *Li*, the word for "common carp," is a homophone for the word *li* meaning "ritual propriety," a necessary attribute of the Confucian scholar-official, as well as for the *li* meaning "advantage" or "benefit." *Li yu*, then, is a rebus for "an abundance of advantage" and, by inference, "affluence."[2]

So the dish in the form of the common carp has both Daoist and Confucian implications for the Chinese. This fish, furthermore, was a favorite decorative motif of the Ming literati because it symbolized successful passage of the imperial civil service examination. Its association and meaning is similar in Japan despite the absence of imperial examinations there. The carp returns upriver to spawn and was therefore conventionally depicted "cresting sprays of white water or mounting waterfalls."[3] Due to the exertion this feat demanded, the carp was associated in Japan with manly vigor.

The carp's body is decorated with relatively carefully delineated scales. Two lower fins are painted on its white belly. On the back of the dish, the head and eye are outlined with single blue lines, and the lines of the dorsal fin and a lower fin are executed with short, neat brushstrokes. The back is also decorated with cobalt pigment blown through a bamboo tube, creating an effect some-

times referred to as *soufflé* blue or *fukizumi*, literally "blown ink" in Japanese. The dish rests on three stubby feet, unglazed on their bottoms. There are *mushikui*, "moth-eaten" edges on the snout, dorsal fin, and forked tail , and the body of the carp bears a firing crack.

1. Burton Watson, trans., *The Complete Works of Chuang Tzu* (New York: Columbia University Press, 1968), pp. 188–89. See also Little, *Taoism and the Arts of China*, p. 124.
2. I am indebted to J. May Lee Barrett for this translation.
3. Baird, *Symbols of Japan*, p. 126.

25. Dish

青花鱼形盘

Ming dynasty, ca. 1625–1635
Porcelain decorated in underglaze cobalt blue
H. 3.8 cm; W. 18.3 cm; D. 9.8 cm
Lent by the Asian Art Museum;
　　Effie B. Allison Collection, Gift of
　　J.V. West and B.V. Gewald (B81P34)

Dishes of this type (Jp: *mukozuke*) and shape were made only for the Japanese market, to be used in sets of five or ten for the *kaiseki* meal that accompanies the tea ceremony. This particular fish (*Siniperca chuatsi*) is also called the Chinese perch or mandarin fish.[1] The Chinese word for "fish," *yu*, is a homophone for the word meaning

"abundance"; fish of various varieties are among the most common motifs on Yuan and Ming paintings and in the decorative arts. The Chinese perch, or *gui yu*, is sometimes depicted with three other fish: the black carp, *qing yu*; the common carp, *li yu*; and the silver carp, *bai lian*. These four fish make up the Chinese rebus *qing bai li gui*, "purity, morality, and nobility of character." The depiction of the black carp and the silver carp form a rebus for the pure (Ch: *qingbai*), or spotless, official who refused bribes.[2] In Japan, the realistic treatment of specific types of fish in art, as on this and the previous *mukozuke* (cat. no. 24) in the exhibition, is usually devoid of symbolism.[3]

The little dish is heavily potted of clay with many impurities; large pinholes have burst through the greyish-blue glaze. *Mushikui* are visible along its bottom edge, under its mouth, and on the back side of the tail. The fish is painted in a moderately good cobalt blue; the depiction of the scales on its side is unusual. There is no decoration on the back, which is glazed except on the bottoms of its four stubby feet.

1. I am indebted to Terese Tse Bartholomew for this identification. See also Eskenazi, *Two Rare Chinese Porcelain Fish Jars*, p. 25.
2. Ibid., pp. 27–28.
3. Baird, *Symbols of Japan*, p. 140.

26. Dish
青花人形盤
Ming dynasty, ca. 1625–1635
Porcelain decorated in underglaze cobalt blue
H. 3.4 cm; W. 18 cm; D. 11 cm
Private Collection

This rare dish (Jp: *mukozuke*) in the form of a man must represent a specific type of human figure. An almost identical dish illustrated in Kawahara's *Ko-sometsuke* book is more clearly defined and aids in the description of this dish.[1] The man wears a close fitting hat and a large hoop earring and holds a large round object in his right hand. He also wears a long robe and a fur pouch with a bow and dangling ribbons. His left foot sticks out from beneath the robe. Alas, this figure fits no description of any of the Buddhist lohan (Ch: *luohan*; Jp: *rakan*) or Chinese immortals (Ch: *xian*; Jp: *sennin*) who appear in Japanese art or any of the indigenous Japanese deities or immortals, partly because the man lacks discernable attributes. His very coarse facial features—round eyes, large nose, and prominent jaw—bring to mind *nanban byobu*, depictions on Japanese screens of the "exotic foreigners," mainly Portuguese, who came to Japan in the late sixteenth and early seventeenth centuries to trade. The facial features of one of a group of three men on a *nanban* screen in the Mary and Jackson Burke Collection closely resemble those depicted on this dish.[2]

The figure's face, earrings, arm, pouch, and ties are outlined in thin brush strokes. His shoulder and shirt are decorated with *fukizumi*, "blown ink," as is the back of the dish, which is glazed. Outlines of his eyes, nose, ear, mouth, and chin are repeated on the back. The heavily-potted dish sits on four unusually broad feet which are stuck with kiln grit on the unglazed bottoms. There are two firing cracks on the front and a gold repair along the left corner of his robe.

1. Kawahara, *Ko-sometsuke*, vol. 2, *Monochrome Section*, p. 192, plate 736.
2. The right hand screen from a pair in the collection; see close-up in Murase, *Turning Point*, p. 242, no. 121.

27. Dish
青花兔形盘
Ming dynasty, ca. 1625–1635
Porcelain decorated in underglaze cobalt blue
H. 4 cm; W. 16.3 cm
Private Collection

The small dish in the form of a hare came in sets of five or ten and was used for the formal *kaiseki* meal. Dishes of this type (Jp: *mukozuke*) were produced in Jingdezhen only for the Japanese market between about 1620 and 1645.

The hare, a Daoist symbol of immortality, is an attribute of the mythical Chang'e, who stole and ate the pill containing the elixir of immortality. She was banished to the moon for her offense. Chilled by the moon's frigid atmosphere, Chang'e coughed up the outer coating of the elixir, which turned into a hare "as white as the purest jade." Thus the characters *yu tu*, "Jade Hare," float above the hare depicted on round *kosometsuke* dishes (cat. no. 95). Forever after, the immortal Chang'e would award a branch of *Osmanthus fragrans* (also known as the cassia tree) to successful graduates of China's imperial civil service examinations from her moon palace, and the jade hare would pound the elixir of immortality by her side.

The animal's head, eyes, and ears are outlined on the front of the dish, which is decorated with *fukizumi*, "blown ink." Its head, eyes, whiskers, and ears are outlined on the bottom, which is also lightly decorated with *fukizumi*. The dish sits on three stubby feet and is heavily potted of clay containing many impurities. A few areas of glaze have flaked off the rim of the dish, revealing a body fired a faint orange.

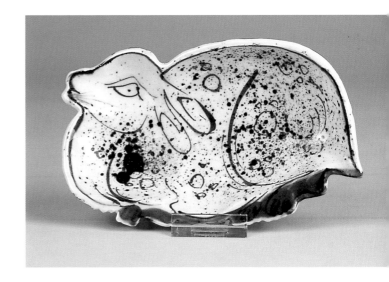

28. Dish

青花牛形盘

Ming dynasty, ca. 1628–1635
Porcelain decorated in underglaze cobalt blue
H. 4 cm; W. 17.8 cm; D. 9.7 cm
Private Collection

This ox with a rather quizzical expression on its face may have been produced by the same kiln that produced the *mukozuke* in the form of a horse from the Allison Collection (cat. no. 30). Like all these shaped dishes, including those of melon shape, it would have been one of a set of five or more used to serve food during the tea ceremony. In China, the ox has been revered for countless centuries. It is the symbol of spring and of agriculture, a patient beast of burden which pulled the plow for peasants affluent enough to feed one. Oxen have also long been associated with water. In very early China, figures of oxen were placed in rivers as talismans when dykes threatened to give way.[1] In Japan, the ox has similar connotations, and its image was used as a talisman against smallpox and other illnesses. It is also linked with Buddhist deities such as Emma (Ch: Yanmowang; Sanskrit: Yama), most prominent among the ten Buddhist kings of hell in Japan.[2]

The ox's head, eyes, nose, whiskers, front and rear legs, and tail are delineated in dark cobalt and filled in with an only slightly lighter blue. Its head and horns are outlined on the back of the dish; front and back are embellished with *fukizumi*, "blown ink." The dish is very heavily potted and covered with a glaze of grey-blue tone. The body consists of very coarsely levigated light grey clay with many impurities; pinholes pierce the glaze on the front and back. The ox rests on three small feet with unglazed bottoms.

1. Wolfram Eberhard, *A Dictionary of Chinese Symbols: Hidden Symbols in Chinese Life and Thought* (London and New York: Routledge and Kegan Paul, 1986), p. 223.
2. Baird, *Symbols of Japan*, pp. 153–54, 189.

29. Dish

青花象形盘

Ming dynasty, ca. 1625–1635
Porcelain decorated in underglaze cobalt blue
H. 4.4 cm; W. 18.2 cm
Private Collection

This heavily-potted dish, *mukozuke*, is made in the form of an elephant and would have been part of a set of five created for serving food during the Japanese tea ceremony. In a Chinese secular context, this large creature is a symbol of strength and wisdom. The white elephant is a particularly important Buddhist symbol. On another dish in the exhibition (cat. no. 103), it is depicted carrying a box surrounded by an aura, probably indicating that the contents are Buddhist scriptures. The elephant was known metaphorically as a vehicle for propagating the Buddhist faith. In China and Japan, Samantabhadra (Ch: Puxian; Jp: Fugen), the Bodhisattva of Universal Virtue, is sometimes depicted riding a white elephant.

On the front of the dish, the recumbent elephant is depicted with brushwork only. Its head, huge ears, tusks, haunches, legs, and tail are outlined in thick strokes and covered in blue washes; the volume of its back is indicated by four vertical blue lines. The back of the dish is extraordinarily different; the elephant's head, tusks, trunk, tail, and the contour of his back are all molded and lightly carved. Only the ears and one of his small, benevolent eyes are embellished with underglaze blue. The very heavily-potted dish is covered with a thick, bluish-white glaze with many imperfections, and it has a few firing cracks. Kiln grit has adhered to the back as well as to the three unglazed feet. The dish has a few *mushikui*.

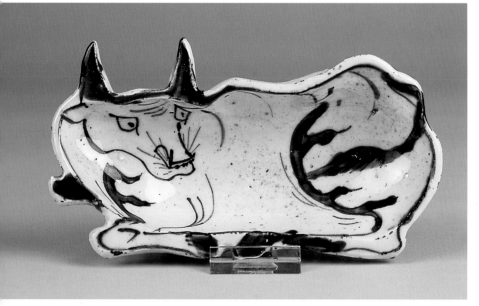

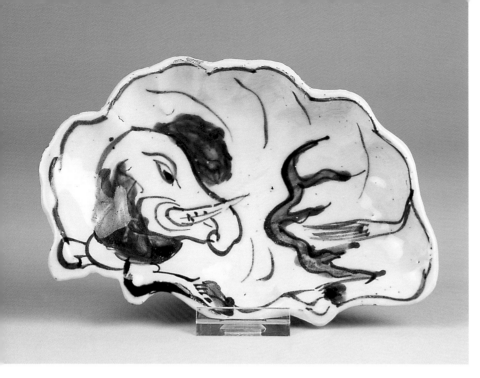

ens to meet with Xiwangmu, Queen Mother of the West.[1] In Shinto, horses helped to control rainfall and conveyed messages between mortals and the gods of heaven.[2] In China and Japan, the horse is the seventh animal represented in the zodiac.

The horse's head, mane, haunches, legs, and tail are outlined in dark blue and filled in with lighter blue. Its eye is painted on a sinister slant, and its open mouth shows several teeth. The front and back of the dish are lightly decorated with *fukizumi*, or "blown ink." The dish is heavily potted and has pinholes in the heavy glaze of bluish tone. It rests on four stubby feet with unglazed bottoms. This *mukozuke* may have been made by the same kiln that produced the ox-shaped dish in the exhibition (cat. no. 28).

1. C.A.S. Williams, *Outlines of Chinese Symbolism and Art Motives*, 3rd. rev. ed. (New York: Dover Publications, 1976), pp. 224–26.
2. Baird, *Symbols of Japan*, p.144.

30. Dish

青花马形盘

Ming dynasty, ca. 1625–1630
Porcelain decorated in underglaze cobalt blue.
H. 4 cm; W. 16.9 cm; D. 10.8 cm
Lent by the Asian Art Museum; Effie B. Allison Collection, Gift of J.V. West and B.V. Gewald (B81P26)

This dish (Jp: *mukozuke*) in the shape of a recumbent horse is part of a set of five or ten dishes generally used to serve fish at the beginning of the *kaiseki*. In China, the horse connotes perseverance and speed. The eight horses of King Mu (10th c. BCE) were a favorite motif on seventeenth-century Chinese porcelains made for the domestic market. They each had specific names and talents and conveyed him around his kingdom and through the heav-

31. Dish

青花龙形盘

Ming dynasty, ca. 1625–1635
Porcelain decorated in underglaze cobalt blue
H. 4 cm; W. 19 cm
Private Collection

The dish (Jp: *mukozuke*) in the form of a winged dragon, was one of a set of five or ten dishes made for serving food during the Japanese tea ceremony. *Mukozuke* in the form of animals, plants, and inanimate objects were made in Jingdezhen exclusively for export to Japan. They were also produced in a wide variety of other forms, including shells, fans, and lutes. The dragon is the symbol of the East; it is associated with sunrise, fertility, and spring rains and has always been a symbol of water and the sea. By the Han dynasty (206 BCE–220 CE), the dragon had also become a symbol of the emperor of China as an omnipotent benevolent force who brought abundance to his dominions. The Japanese adopted these associations from the Chinese, as well as the Chinese substitution of the dragon for the Indian *naga* deities, or serpent gods, "viewed as protectors of the Buddhist faith and associated with rain, clouds and thunder."[1]

The dragon on this dish has the horns of a deer, the scales of a snake, lappets which turn into chevrons by his chest, spiky eyebrows over beady eyes, thick whiskers, and prominent fangs. The heavily-potted dish is covered with a thick blue-green glaze. Its back is undecorated except for the molded eye, mouth, and whiskers around the mouth. The dish rests on four stubby feet, the bottoms of which are unglazed but covered with kiln grit. One of the dragon's feet sports a gold lacquer repair.

1. Baird, *Symbols of Japan*, p. 133.

32. Dish
青花瑞鸟形盘
Ming dynasty, ca. 1625–1635
Porcelain decorated in underglaze cobalt blue
H. 4.8 cm; W. 16.8 cm; D. 13.3 cm
Lent by the Asian Art Museum; Effie B. Allison
    Collection, Gift of J.V. West and B.V. Gewald
    (B81P33)

This amazing, rare bird dish would have been part of a set of food dishes, *mukozuke*, made exclusively for the Japanese market. The bird is depicted with a long beak and prominently colored feathers on the ends of its wings and tail. Because the bird clutches a peach in its talons, it is undoubtedly a crane. Both the peach and the crane are attributes of Shou Lao, the Chinese god of immortality, who from the Tianqi through early Kangxi eras

(1621–1679) is frequently depicted on Chinese porcelains flying on his crane to meet the Eight Daoist Immortals. His counterparts in Japan, Jurojin and Fukurokuju, symbolize learning and wisdom as well as longevity.[1]

The crane dish is heavily potted of rather coarse clay. It is covered in a thick greyish glaze except where the glaze has flaked off or was not applied—on the bottoms of the four stubby feet and on the lumps which festoon its underside. Either way, the bottom of the dish is unpainted and unusually lumpy. A firing crack appears on the bird's right wing and on a peach leaf; pinholes from the coarse clay body pierce the glaze on the inside and on the bottom.

1. Baird, *Symbols of Japan*, pp. 199–200.

33. Plate

青花天啓款山水人物纹圆盘
Ming dynasty, Tianqi mark and period (1621–1627)
Porcelain decorated in underglaze cobalt blue
H. 2.3 cm; Diam. 14.6 cm
Private Collection

By the Ming dynasty, symmetry dominated the arts in China, so that the asymmetrical arrangement of rondels on the rim of this dish announces that it was made in Jingdezhen for export to Japan. Three rondels are decorated with prunus in reserve, and three with chevrons and crosses in reserve. The landscape in the center of the dish would have suited Chinese as well as Japanese patrons. It is fashioned in the style of late Wanli period export ware (ca. 1600–1620). In the foreground, two scholars stand on a high bridge connected to a promontory near a viewing pavilion. Water is indicated on the porcelain's white ground with a few blue striations and a rock in the middle of the composition. A deciduous tree hangs over the water and leads the eye into the middle and far distance, indicated by undulating promontories each with a tree perched on top. The leaves on the three trees are depicted with dark cobalt washes, blobs rather than dark blue outlines covered with washes. The potter-painters made no attempt to create recession by reducing the size of the promontories; all similar landscape elements are the same size, but this gives the scene an immediacy often lacking in landscapes painted on porcelains.

The rim of the dish is thinly potted of very white clay covered with a refined, glassy glaze that has a blue-green tinge. The shallow foot ring is hastily beveled and has a few bits of kiln grit. Pieces of clay detached from the inside foot ring and clung to the glaze on the bottom of the dish during firing. The bottom bears a four-character mark in clerical script encircled by two blue lines; it reads *Tianqi nian zhi*, "made in the reign of Tianqi."

34. Plate
青花天啓款花卉纹圆盘
Ming dynasty, Tianqi mark and period (1621–1627)
Porcelain decorated in underglaze cobalt blue
H. 2.7 cm; Diam. 21.4 cm
Lent by the Asian Art Museum; Effie B. Allison
    Collection, Gift of J.V. West and B.V. Gewald
    (B81P38)

This relatively small, well-potted plate is decorated with six rondels covering less than half the plate's rim. This asymmetrical arrangement immediately signals the destination of this dish and others like it as Japan. The rondels contain prunus, or plum, blossoms in relief on a blue ground. The center of the dish is decorated with a large tree peony, a chrysanthemum with two blossoms, a wasp, and a dragonfly silhouetted against a plain ground. The tree peony (Ch: *mudan*; Jp: *botan*), also known as *fugui hua*, "the flower of wealth and rank," is used in rebuses about prosperity.[1] The chrysanthemum (Ch: *juhua*; Jp: *kiku*), symbol of autumn, also alludes to the fourth-century Chinese scholar-official and recluse Tao Qian (Tao Yuanming; 365–427), who abandoned his official post to return to his family farm and pass his time writing poetry and drinking chrysanthemum wine. In Japan, the flower's association with Tao Qian led to its

connection with reclusion as well as with writing poetry and drinking wine in secluded settings.[2] The dragonfly (Jp: *tombo*) in Japan is associated with success in military endeavors; various Japanese names for the insect are homophones for "victory."[3] The word for "wasp" (Ch: *feng*; Jp: *hachi*) is a homophone in Chinese for *feng*, meaning to confer a title. In combination with other animals and insects, the wasp is a part of several Chinese rebuses about rank and riches, but in Japan the wasp has no general iconographical significance.[4]

The body of this plate is composed of well-levigated clay covered in a glassy glaze of bluish tone. Its back is decorated with four circles, or pearls, infilled with medium blue wash, each surrounded by three dark dots. The foot ring is shallow and undercut. The bottom is glazed, and chatter marks can be seen under the glaze, which has pulled away from the foot in places. It bears the typical four-character mark *Tianqi nian zhi*, "made in the reign of Tianqi," in regular script surrounded by two blue lines.

1. Terese Tse Bartholomew, *Myths and Rebuses in Chinese Art* (San Francisco: The Museum, 1988), p. 11; Baird, *Symbols of Japan*, pp. 60–61.
2. Baird, *Symbols of Japan*, pp. 74–75.
3. Ibid., p. 108.
4. Ibid., p. 121.

35. Bowl

青花五彩天啓款碗

Ming dynasty, Tianqi mark and period
   (1621–1627)
Porcelain decorated in underglaze
   cobalt blue and polychrome enamels
H. 4.7 cm; Diam. 14.4 cm
Private Collection

This bowl is a brilliant example of the asymmetrical aesthetic adopted by Jingdezhen potters from 1620 to 1645 to suit Japanese taste. The center scene depicts a pine with gnarled trunk, twisted branches, and clumps of dark needles perched on rocky hillock. A stunted bamboo grows beside it, and iron-red clouds and a red sun hover overhead. Another sun, painted in underglaze blue, hangs between pine boughs. On the cavetto and rim of the bowl, sprays of tree peony explode in a riot of colors— cobalt blue, iron-red, green, and yellow enamels. A five-character poem beside the tree peony descends down the cavetto. The decoration on the bowl depicts the "three friends of winter," (Ch: *suihan sanyou*) linked together in Chinese paintings, poetry, and decorative arts since the Southern Song (1127–1279).[1] Pine, prunus, and bamboo (Jp: *shōchikubai*) brave the rigors of winter and thus signify courage, endurance, and integrity, attributes of "the cultured gentleman."[2] The "three friends," which decorate many *kosometsuke* wares, remain a favored motif to this day in Japan.

   The bowl has an everted rim covered with many *mushikui* and four tiny firing cracks. It is heavily potted and covered with a thick bluish-green glaze. Two sprays of prunus in underglaze blue and iron red decorate either side of the cavetto on the outside of the bowl. The unglazed foot ring is shallow and very hastily beveled; kiln grit adheres to it almost all the way around, and chatter marks are visible inside the foot. A four-character mark reading *Tianqi nian zhi*, "made in the reign of Tianqi," is written in clerical script and surrounded by two blue lines on the glazed bottom.

1. Maggie Bickford, *Ink Plum: the Making of a Chinese Scholar-Painting Genre* (Cambridge: Cambridge University Press, 1996), p. 36.
2. Baird, *Symbols of Japan*, p. 66.

36. Plate

青花山水人物纹圆盘

Ming dynasty, ca. 1630–1645
Porcelain decorated in underglaze cobalt blue
H. 2.9 cm; Diam. 21.2 cm
Lent by the Asian Art Museum; Effie B. Allison
   Collection, Gift of J.V. West and B.V. Gewald
   (B81P6)

This extraordinary plate is an excellent example of "Momoyama aesthetics reflected" on Jingdezhen

kosometsuke wares of the late Ming period.[1] Only a fourth of the rim and cavetto are decorated with chevron and petal-shaped borders; the rest is left unadorned except for borders of single blue lines below the rim and at the top of the cavetto and two blue lines around the center scene. Contained within a five-lobed frame, the scene in the center depicts three figures, each carrying two buckets on a pole over their shoulders. Promontories with huts on them loom over the figures, and pines arch over the void at the top of the scene.

Yoshiko Kakudo illustrated this plate in her catalogue of the Effie B. Allison Collection.[2] A third plate, illustrated by Kawahara, is substantially different, containing figures, all apparently female, dressed in long robes and carrying buckets on poles over their shoulders. Both Kawahara and Kilburn refer to the story illustrated on these plates as the "brine-dripping" (Jp: *shiokume*) scene, a dance in which a young maiden gathered seawater (brine) to make salt.[3] But the Chinese potters may have painted the figures to look more like men than women. In fact, the scene may be based on the Noh play *Matsukaze*, in which two sisters who gather brine in Suma, on the Inland Sea, fall in love with a young courtier briefly exiled there. Even as ghosts, the sisters await his return, "Constant ever, green as a pine," until their spirits are at last freed by the prayers of a priest.[4] The plate may depict the two sisters on either side of the taller courtier.

The plate is well potted of fairly well-levigated clay. The cobalt used to decorate the plate is quite dark, and the scene is painted in typical broad-brush fashion, outlined, and filled in mostly with dark wash. Some kiln grit adheres to the unglazed foot ring and inside the glazed bottom. The back of the plate is decorated with two flaming pearls and two lozenges; two blue lines surround the foot, and a single blue line encircles the rim.

1. Kakudo, *The Effie B. Allison Collection*, p.25.
2. Ibid., p. 25, no. 25.
3. See Kawahara, *Ko-sometsuke*, vol. 2, *Monochrome Section*, nos. 600, 601; Richard Kilburn, *Transitional Wares and Their Forerunners* (Hong Kong: Oriental Ceramic Society of Hong Kong, 1981), p. 166, no. 131.
4. Paul Varley, *Japanese Culture* (Honolulu: University of Hawaii Press, 2000), pp. 117–18.

37. Dish
青花菊纹花口盘
Ming dynasty, ca. 1630–1645
Porcelain decorated in underglaze cobalt blue
H. 3 cm; Diam. 21 cm
Butler Family Collection

This elegant dish with a foliated rim is perhaps the most subtly decorated of all the dishes in the exhibition. A large chrysanthemum leaf arches asymmetrically over the interior. The left side of the leaf's top lobe has a key fret, or thunderbolt, pattern painted on it; this pattern was used to decorate Japanese textiles of the early seventeenth century and appeared on the borders of *kraak* porcelains produced from 1600 to the 1640s.[1] The two left lobes are turned inward, and the left side of the top right lobe is painted with a spiky chrysanthemum blossom and curlicues. Below the leaf, a blossom is depicted from the back, and a recently opened chrysanthemum and leaf are attached to the bottom of the stem. Large chrysanthemum blossoms are incised on the interior of the dish under a thick but refined white glaze of bluish tint. As in China, the chrysanthemum became a symbol of autumn in Japan as well as of reclusion and poetry writing. The flower was associated with the fourth-century Chinese poet and scholar official Tao Qian. Tao left his official position and returned to his family's farm to write poetry, cultivate his chrysanthemums, and drink wine.[2]

The reverse of the dish is decorated with a vigorous scrolling vine and tendrils and flowers with oblong petals, perhaps what is known in Chinese as *baoxiang hua*, "treasure flower" or "foreign lotus."[3] The shallow, beveled foot is unglazed and the bottom glazed. Large bits of kiln grit adhere to the glaze all the way around the outside and inside of the foot. The glaze is more carefully refined than on most wares made in Jingdezhen for the Japanese market. The bottom bears a *fu*, "happiness," mark in underglaze-blue seal script. It lacks the double square or rectangle which generally surrounds the *fu* marks on wares made for Japan in this era.

1. See, for example, Amanda Meyer Stinchecum, *Kosode: 16th–19th Century Textiles from the Noruma Collection* (New York: Japan Society and Kodansha International, 1984), p. 91, detail of color-plate 5; Maura Rinaldi, "Dating Kraak Porcelain," in "Kraak begeerlijk porselein uit China," *Vormen uit Vuur* 180/181 (2003/1–2), pp. 34, 37, 39.
2. Baird, *Symbols of Japan*, pp. 75–76.
3. Bartholomew, "Botanical Motifs in Chinese Furniture," pp. 41–43.

branches of a tree peony painted in underglaze cobalt blue with one peony blossom and two buds depicted in underglaze copper red. The two fields are painted with opposing centers of gravity; as the crane flies up the bowl, the peony spray hangs down.

This bowl, which must have been one of a set of five or more, is a technological tour de force. The copper red peony has fired a perfect pink, and the *fukizumi* in the sky around the crane and the roiling waves beneath the peony spray are perfectly controlled. The bowl is heavily potted of well-levigated white clay. It has many *mushikui*, or "moth-eaten" edges, on the rim. The glaze is heavy but refined; it has a grey-blue cast except on the bottom, where it is whiter. There is no foot ring; the bottom has been undercut, and the bowl rests on an unglazed circle. Bowls of this form but with very different decoration were found on the Hatcher wreck, which was probably sunk in 1643.[1]

1. See the first auction of The Hatcher Collection; Christie's Amsterdam B.V, *Fine and important late Ming and transitional porcelain* (Amsterdam, 14 March 1984), lots 259, 260, illus. p. 47.

38. Bowl

青花釉里红瑞鹤纹碗

Ming dynasty, ca. 1635–1645
Porcelain decorated in underglaze cobalt blue
    and copper red
H. 4.5 cm; Diam. 14.8 cm
Butler Family Collection

This small deep bowl illustrates the Japanese decorative technique known as *katami-gawari*, "alternating sides," in which two contrasting designs are used to decorate the interior. The technique was used on Japanese lacquers, Oribe and other ceramic wares, and textiles of the late sixteenth and early seventeenth centuries. *Katami-gawari* decoration usually employs lines to separate the fields, but on this bowl the fields are separated by the white ground of the glazed porcelain. On one side of the bowl, a crane is pictured in flight; the blue tips of its wings are mostly obscured by the *fukizumi*, or *soufflé* blue, ground against which it flies. Its long legs proceed up the bowl's cavetto in defiance of gravity. On the opposite side, roiling waves depicted in *soufflé* blue support two

39. Dish

青花五彩花卉纹圆盘

Ming dynasty, ca. 1635–1645
Porcelain decorated in underglaze cobalt blue
    and polychrome enamels
H. 3 cm; Diam. 14.5 cm
Butler Family Collection

This dish is apparently the sole survivor of a set of five dishes probably used for serving food during the *kaiseki*, a small meal served during the tea ceremony. The decoration in the center is divided by a straight blue line in a technique of contrasting fields known in Japanese as *katami-gawari*, "alternating sides." This technique was widely used in Japan on Kodaiji lacquerware and on Oribe wares of the late sixteenth and early seventeenth centuries, and a similar technique was used on textiles of that era.[1] In China, Jingdezhen potters used this decorative technique exclusively on wares produced for the Japanese market.

The rim of the dish is decorated with an iron-red key fret, or thunderbolt, border enclosed between two blue lines. The center is divided into two fields with floral motifs. On the right, painted in underglaze blue and iron-red, yellow, and green enamels, are the "three friends of

winter": pine, prunus, and bamboo. These "three friends" brave the elements; the pine and bamboo remain green through winter, and the prunus is the first to blossom despite frost and even snow. Singled out in China for their resistance to climatic adversity, these three plants came to connote attributes of the scholar-official: endurance, perseverance, and integrity or purity. On the left side of the dish, incised white chrysanthemum blossoms float against a blue ground decorated in reserve with three white lotus buds and scrolling vines. In a Chinese and Japanese Buddhist context, the lotus is the flower of purity and integrity because it rises spotless through the mud of the lotus pond.[2] And in China, the chrysanthemum, which braves the elements in the fall to bloom in the cold, symbolizes autumn and connotes integrity and reclusion. The flower is associated with the fourth-century poet Tao Qian, who left his official post and returned home to write poetry and drink chrysanthemum wine. Later, in Japan, the flower became linked "to the intertwined activities of poetry writing and wine drinking in secluded mountain settings."[3]

The back of the dish is decorated with a single blue-line border under the rim and another line which runs around the outside of the foot and trails off onto the back of the cavetto. Like a number of small *ko'akae* dishes made around 1635 or so, circular impressions created by the pressure of the potter's hands or a tool while the dish was on the wheel can be seen on the back of the dish.[4] The foot ring is unglazed and hastily beveled. Sizable patches of kiln grit adhere to the glazed bottom inside the foot. The dish bears a *fu*, "happiness," mark in seal script enclosed by a rectangular cartouche of two blue lines.

1. See Murase, *Turning Point*, nos. 73, 143, 144, 147, 152, 153; 163, 164.
2. Baird, *Symbols of Japan*, p. 88.
3. Ibid., pp 75–76.
4. The term "*ko'akae* wares," literally "old colored wares" in Japanese, refers to porcelain produced in Jingdezhen and decorated with underglaze cobalt blue and polychrome enamels or with enamels only. The *ko'akae* wares illustrated in this catalogue share potting characteristics and painting techniques which allow art historians to date their manufacture between about 1625 and 1645.

40. Dish

青花五彩负笈行旅图圆盘

Ming dynasty, ca. 1630–1635
Porcelain decorated in underglaze cobalt blue
    and polychrome enamels
H. 2.5 cm; Diam. 21 cm
Butler Family Collection

The asymmetrical composition of this dish is almost reminiscent of Southern Song fan paintings; the tree on the
upper right and the waves on the lower left bear the
weight of the composition. A male servant with pant-legs
rolled up is carrying a bundle of books on a pole over his
left shoulder. Under a tree whose branches are intertwined
with horizontal clouds painted in iron red and underglaze
blue, the servant makes his way along a shore dotted with
rocks and flowers and looks over a semi-circular mass of
waves painted in underglaze blue and green enamel and
topped with iron-red foam. The delicacy of the underglaze blue, the sparseness of the composition, and the care
and spontaneity with which the enamels are applied give
the dish a charm unusual in the body of *ko'akae* wares.

    The dish has a brown-glazed foliated rim. On the
body, the glaze has a bluish tinge; inside the foot, the glaze
is whiter. The rounded foot is unglazed and roughly finished, and kiln sand and grit are stuck to the foot and the
bottom. Where the glaze has pulled away inside the foot,
a light orange body is revealed. The *fu*, "happiness," mark
written in seal script on the bottom is enclosed within a
double square and surrounded by a single blue line.

41. Dish

青花釉里红鸿雁纹圆盘

Ming dynasty, ca. 1635–1645
Porcelain decorated in underglaze cobalt blue
    and iron red
H. 2.5 cm; Diam. 14.5 cm
Private Collection

This dish, with its unevenly scalloped border and dense
ground covered with diaper designs, is a harbinger of a
later Japanese style of Chinese export ware made for
Japan: Shonzui ware. But its potting characteristics and
the painting of the geese claim common ground with
other porcelains in the exhibition. And the dish is a splendid example of the Japanese love of juxtaposed contrasting patterns which cover the entire surface of an
object. In a decorative technique described as "the angular division of fields,"[1] *katami-gawari* in Japanese, the
ground on this dish is divided into five wedges, each decorated with a different diaper pattern—interlocking Y-
shapes, lappets or waves, basket weave, lozenges with
floral stamens, and interlocking petal shapes. Six rondels
are superimposed on this visually complex ground, each
containing a white goose.

    A migratory flock of geese often connotes autumn
and separation, and thus the goose is a symbol of parting.[2]
In Japan, the eighth lunar month is known as the month
of the goose's return, *kanraigetsu*, referring to the migra-
tion of geese. Following the lead of Northern Song

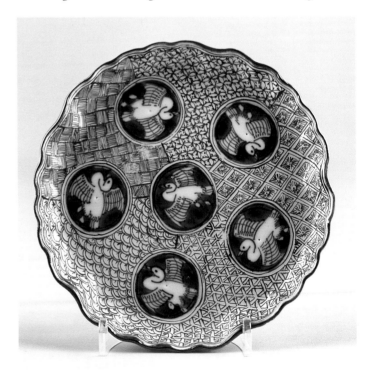

painters of the eleventh century who painted views of the Xiao and Xiang rivers with flocks of geese departing or descending to land, Japanese landscape painters incorporated this theme into scenes of lakes and rivers. Geese also became known as saviors of Japanese military leaders alerted to ambush by a sudden change in the formation of a flock of geese flying overhead. This association led to the adoption of the goose in family crests; the design on this dish is evocative of such usage. In Japan, folk belief also connected the goose to marital happiness.[3]

Like many of the ko'akae wares in the exhibition, the rim of the dish is covered with a brown glaze. The dish is well potted and covered with a medium thick glaze of blue-green cast which has pooled above the foot. The bottom is glazed but the glaze had pulled away from the top of the foot ring two thirds of the way around the foot. Chunks of kiln grit mar the underside of the dish and cling to the glaze above the unglazed, beveled foot ring. The dish bears a very sketchy apocryphal six-character Chenghua (1465–1487) mark on the bottom.

1. Baird, *Symbols of Japan*, p. 290.
2. Eberhard, *A Dictionary of Chinese Symbols*, p. 132.
3. Baird, *Symbols of Japan*, pp. 111–12, 308–9.

42. Dish

青花釉里红参禅罗汉图圆盘

Ming dynasty, ca. 1635–1645
Porcelain decorated in underglaze cobalt blue
 and polychrome enamels
H. 3.4 cm; Diam. 15.2 cm
Private Collection

This dish with a brown-glazed foliated rim illustrates the Jingdezhen potters' use of asymmetry to organize the center scene and intricate diaper borders. The center of the dish is dominated by the figure of a lohan (Ch: *luohan*; Jp: *rakan*) in a green robe seated on a mat decorated with iron-red spokes and aubergine-enameled fringe. Because there are no attributes around him, he cannot be identified by name. The lohan sits on the right under a horizontal iron-red cloud and beside green and yellow rocks. A twisted aubergine trunk rises and branches out with green leaves above the figure. The left side of the scene is undecorated.

The center scene is surrounded by a foliate frame like the one on a dish decorated with a mounted scholar (cat. no. 69); the frame consists of six different diaper patterns contained within blue double-line ogee borders. Three linked swastika diapers painted in underglaze iron red alternate with underglaze-blue diapers in swastika, tortoiseshell, and petal patterns. On the cavetto, three large panels contain depictions of a pine, a prunus, and a bamboo; the pine and prunus hang down from the rim, while the pine springs up from the center of the dish. These three panels alternate with three panels containing a small lobed cartouche, each framing a different floral spray: a peony, the "king of flowers" in China; the chrysanthemum, symbol of autumn and reclusion; and the lotus, a Buddhist symbol of purity and a Confucian symbol of the "princely man." The interlocking Y-shape, the linked swastika, and the petal diaper decorate the area around the three cartouches.

The dish was finished in a mold placed on a potter's wheel. It is light, potted of well-levigated clay, and covered in a thick blue-grey glaze that has pooled above the foot. Large bits of grey and black grit cling to the glaze outside and inside the foot. The glazed bottom has a few pinholes and bears a *da tang*, "great hall," mark written in seal script in underglaze blue and enclosed in two blue squares.

43. Set of Five Dishes
五彩万花锦纹套盘
Ming dynasty, ca. 1630–1645
Porcelain decorated in polychrome enamels
H. 3.5 cm; W. 13.8 cm
Private Collection

This set of five dishes (Jp: *mukozuke*) bear eloquent testimony to Japanese interest in textile patterning and the influence of this enthusiasm on Jingdezhen porcelain made for the Japanese market between 1620 and 1645. These dishes are decorated with a textile pattern known in Japan as *indo-sarasamon*, "Indian print design."[1] During the seventeenth century, textiles of this design were apparently brought from India to Canton by Arab or Chinese traders and then from Canton to Nagasaki, Japan, by Chinese merchants. The textiles were highly sought after in Japan, especially by court ladies and wives of prominent warlords, or *daimyo*. Textiles containing a purple color were the most highly prized; in the early seventeenth century, Japan had no indigenous source of the

intense Indian purple dye, *bengara-iro* (possibly a corruption of the name Bengal), echoed in the aubergine glaze on these dishes.

Chinese potter-painters and enamellers have skillfully adapted the textile patterns to the surface of the porcelains. The center of the dishes are decorated with a lozenge pattern; lozenges with diaper patterns of Y-shapes, tortoiseshell hexagons, linked swastikas, and asters alternate with side views of prunus and open prunus blossoms painted in two tones of iron-red, aubergine, green, and yellow enamels. Beaded pendants decorate the corners of the cavetto, and a scrolling border of leaves and blossoms decorates the rims. The backs of the dishes are not decorated.

The dishes are very heavily potted of white clay which is full of impurities. They are covered in a thick glaze with a slight blue-green tinge; all have a few *mushikui* on the rims. The bottoms are glazed; the thick, unglazed foot rings are beveled and have small bits of kiln grit adhering to them. Spots of green enamel were splattered on four of the dishes. On one dish, the iron-rich body had fired a bright orange where two large spots on the exterior are unglazed. The square foot rings are all askew.

1. Christie, Manson & Woods, *The Peony Pavilion Collection: Chinese Tea Ceramics for Japan* (c. 1580–1650) (London, 12 June, 1989), p. 98.

44. Dish
五彩花口盘
Ming dynasty, ca. 1630–1645
Porcelain decorated in polychrome enamels
H. 3.4 cm; Diam. 20.5 cm
Private Collection

At odds with the austere tea taste of late sixteenth-century Japan, this well painted hexagonal dish with chamfered rim is testimony to the catholic taste of the Japanese in the early Edo period (1615–1868), a taste for colorful, densely decorated textiles, lacquer, and porcelain.[1] The center scene is decorated with a white heron (Ch: *lu*: Jp: *sagi*) gazing up at an enormous lotus, emblematic of purity, with three large blossoms, pods, a green lotus leaf, and a large frilly leaf painted in dark aubergine enamel. Arrowroot and millet are commingled with the lotus; bamboo springs from behind green and yellow rocks which frame the aquatic scene. The flowers, plants, and birds are largely outlined in iron red and skillfully filled in with green, yellow, turquoise, and dark aubergine enamels. At the top of the scene, an impetuous quail dives

downward; the entire spectacle is a riot of color and movement. This scene contains two possible rebuses. A heron combined with a fresh lotus (Ch: *qing lian*) forms the rebus for *yilu qinglian*, "may your entire path (Ch: *yilu*) be honest and upright (Ch: *qinglian*)," a reference to incorruptible officials. The quail (Ch: *anchun*) pictured with a single heron forms the rebus for *yilu ping'an*, "may your entire way be peaceful."

Nor is the cavetto an anticlimax. It is decorated with six cartouches containing aquatic animals. There is a three-legged toad, which must belong to the Daoist immortal Liu Haichan (Jp: Gama Sennin), with bulging eyes, iron-red lips, and aubergine spots. The crab is painted in great detail including hairy claws and bug eyes. A snail, or sea slug, fresh water shrimp, a common carp with whiskers, and a turtle complete the group.[2] Most appear on other *ko'akae* porcelains in the exhibition. The lobed cartouches they occupy are surrounded by diaper pattern borders: the fish by lappets, the crab by a yellow Y-shapes, the sea snail by petals, the shrimp by green crosses, the turtle by interlocking swastikas, and the toad by a hexagons in a tortoiseshell pattern. The dish is a tour de force of Jingdezhen enamellers' art.

The dish was finished on a mold placed on the potter's wheel; the potter's hand created grooves around the reverse of the cavetto as he finished the dish. It is heavily potted and covered by a thick grey glaze. The foot is shallow, undercut, and very hastily finished and is littered with large brown and grey chunks of kiln grit. Its glazed bottom is decorated with a *fu*, "happiness," mark in seal script surrounded by two rectangles in dark underglaze blue.

1. This catholicity also characterized the tea taste of the Momoyama period (1573–1615), according to Taishu Komatsu in Murase, *Turning Point*, p. 290.
2. For an image of the *li yu* carp (*Cyprinus carpio carpio*) after an illustration in the famous Ming dynasty *Bencao gangmu* [Compendium of Materia Medica], see Eskenazi, *Two Rare Chinese Porcelain Fish Jars*, p. 43, fig. 23.

III. FLORA AND FAUNA IN PORCELAIN DECORATION FOR THE JAPANESE MARKET

45. Dish

五彩花口盘

Ming dynasty, ca. 1625–1635
Porcelain decorated in polychrome enamels
H. 3.6 cm; Diam. 20.5 cm
Butler Family Collection

This molded hexagonal dish with a lobed rim is painted with the surface clutter typical of late Ming polychrome wares made for the Japanese market. The center is decorated with a Lake Tai rock and a large tree peony bearing a red and a yellow blossom with well delineated petals. A yellow bird sits on a branch of the tree peony, and bamboo sprouts on either side of the rock. Wispy

clouds are painted in the spaces between the tall branches. The cavetto and rim are decorated with alternating sprays of lotus, prunus, and aster, one in each segment of the rim. The lotus is the Buddhist symbol of purity, because it rises clean and white through the mud. The prunus, or plum, is the earliest to bloom in the late winter, pushing through the ice and snow; it is therefore a symbol of perseverance as well as purity. In addition, the five petals of its flower represent the Five Blessings: health, wealth, love of virtue, old age, and a natural death.

The dish is hastily potted and painted in comparison with dishes of the same type and period. In some places, the enamels are applied very thinly and are not always contained within their darker outlines. Long chatter

72

marks are visible on the glazed bottom, which is full of pinholes. The glaze on the bottom has separated from the inside of the unglazed, crudely finished foot. Kiln sand and grit are stuck to the foot and bottom of the dish. The bottom has a *fu*, "happiness," mark inscribed in thick strokes of dark cobalt and surrounded by a single blue line. Bits of green glaze spot the underside of the cavetto.

46. Dish

五彩一路连封纹圆盘

Ming dynasty, ca. 1635–1645
Porcelain decorated in polychrome enamels
H. 3.5 cm; Diam. 15 cm
Butler Family Collection

This molded dish with a brown-glazed foliated rim is decorated with a heron standing in shallow water surrounded by lotus blossoms and leaves, arrowroot, and a wasp, which together form the Chinese rebus *yilu lianfeng*, "continuous promotion." The dish is relatively well potted and covered by a thick, blue-green glaze with a few prominent pinholes. Kiln grit adheres to the shallow, hastily-formed foot. The bottom is glazed, but the glaze has pulled away within the foot ring revealing an orange body. A quickly-written apocryphal six-character Chenghua (1465–1487) mark is inscribed on the bottom in underglaze blue and surrounded by a single blue line. The dish was probably made in the same kiln which made the molded dish decorated with arrowroot plants, a shrimp, and a wasp (cat. no. 47), a design taken from the late Ming dynasty woodblock-illustrated book *Bazhong huapu* [Manual of Eight Styles of Painting].

47. Dish

五彩花口盘

Ming dynasty, ca. 1635–1645
Porcelain decorated in polychrome enamels
H. 3.4 cm; Diam. 15 cm
Butler Family Collection

This foliated dish with brown-glazed rim is decorated with an aquatic scene taken from the woodblock-printed book *Bazhong huapu* [Manual of Eight Styles of Painting], an eight-volume collected work printed in the Tianqi period (1621–1627). The book was also popular in Japan, where it was known as *Hasshu gafu*. It included illustrations of poems about flowers and plants. The scene on this dish is based on the illustration of the poem "Arrowroot" in the sixth volume, entitled *Caobenhua shipu* [Poems and Paintings of Flowering Plants].[1] The dish is quite finely enameled and reflects the print closely. A rocky shore on the right frames the arrowroot plant and blossoms. To the left, a shrimp leaps from the water and an insect buzzes overhead. The weight of the composition is on the right, and the insect fills the void between the aquatic grasses overhead and the arrowroot leaves below.

The dish was probably thrown on a wheel and then pressed into a foliated mold; the circles created by the potter's hands and/or tools are still visible on the back of the dish. Bits of kiln grit adhere to most of the shallow, unglazed foot. The thick, bluish glaze has partly filled a small gash, probably made by a tool, on the reverse of the cavetto. An apocryphal, six-character Chenghua

73

(1465–1487) mark in underglaze blue within a single blue circle is inscribed on its glazed bottom, and a single blue dot hangs below the underside of the rim.

1. Herbert Butz and Kawahara Masahiko, eds., *Chinesische Porzellane des 17. Jahrhunderts für Japan: Sammlung Georg Weishaupt* (Berlin: Museum für Ostasiatische Kunst, 1996), pp. 72–73, no. 38. The illustrations cited by Butz and Kawahara come from a 1710 reprint edition of the *Bazhong huapu*, published in Kyoto and now in the collection of the Berlin Museum for East Asian Art.

48. Dish

青花五彩菊纹圆盘

Ming dynasty, Tianqi mark and period (1621–1627)
Porcelain decorated in underglaze cobalt blue
  and polychrome enamels
H. 3 cm; Diam. 16.5 cm
Butler Family Collection

This dish, decorated with chrysanthemums, a bee, and a poem, would have been one of a set of *mukozuke* dishes. The decoration on the dish consists primarily of six chrysanthemums: three have petals outlined in blue-grey cobalt and are covered with blue wash, while three are outlined in iron red and have yellow-enameled centers. A very large bee, rendered in iron red, flies over a seven-character line of poetic verse written in clerical script. The line reads, *xu zhi jiu ri shi fang rong*, which can be translated "we must realize that only on the Ninth Day [of the Ninth Month, i.e. on the Double Nines Festival] does it [the chrysanthemum] fragrantly flourish." It could be interpreted to imply allegorically that, like the chrysanthemum, virtue takes a long time to flourish.[1] The chrysanthemum is a symbol of autumn; it blossoms later than any other flower, thus connoting perseverance, a trait admired by the Chinese. This flower was much loved by Tao Qian (Tao Yuanming; 365–427), one of China's most esteemed poets. A scholar-official who forsook his official position in order to follow his star, Tao retired to his poor family farm to write poetry, drink wine, and cultivate his chrysanthemums. Tao and the flower thus became synonymous with the upright and reclusive scholar as well as Daoist and Confucian self-cultivation, traits of utmost importance in China and Japan. The bee is a symbol of industry and persistence in promoting growth and prosperity. Traditionally, honey was much cultivated and valued by Buddhist monks in China.[2]

The dish has a small everted rim and is covered in a greyish glaze. Its back is decorated with three flaming pearls; two blue lines surround the foot, and a single blue line encircles the rim. The foot is carelessly beveled and unglazed. The glazed bottom is covered with pinholes; chatter marks are visible under the glaze, and bits of green glaze adhere to the foot and the bottom. A four-character mark, reading *Tianqi nian zhi*, "made in the reign of Tianqi," was written with a loaded brush. The mark is surrounded by two blue lines; below the mark, the glaze has pulled away from the foot ring leaving small holes.

1. My thanks to Prof. Jonathan Chaves, George Washington University, for the translation and its allegorical interpretation.
2. Ong Hean-Tatt, *Chinese Animal Symbolisms* (Petaling Jaya, Selangor Darul Ehsan, Malaysia: Pelanduk Publications, 1993), p. 262.

49. Dish

青花莲纹方盘

Ming dynasty, ca. 1635–1645

Porcelain decorated in underglaze cobalt
blue

H. 3.8 cm; W. 18.7 cm; D. 19.1 cm

Lent by the Asian Art Museum, Gift of
Roy Leventritt (B69P102L)

This square dish (Jp: *mukozuke*) with notched corners was part of a set of five or possibly ten dishes made for the Japanese market. It is decorated with lotus blossoms and wavy grasses in a scene derived, like several other porcelains in the exhibition (cat. nos. 46, 47, 65), from the *Bazhong huapu* [Manual of Eight Types of Painting], a woodblock-printed book of the Tianqi period (1621–1627). The particular source for this dish illustrates "Lotus," the seventh poem in volume six, *Caobenhua shipu* [Poems and Paintings of Flowering Plants].[1]

The potter-painters followed the woodblock-printed illustration closely but substituted a turtle with paws in the air for the frog in the print. Water weeds and a lotus pad float on the water below the low-lying sun while a wasp flies above it. In China and Japan, the lotus in a secular context connotes the Confucian "princely man" because it blooms unstained after rising through the mud and water in which it grows. The four corners of the cavetto are painted with elaborate tassels. Its rim is decorated in reserve with a border of scrolls and chrysanthemum blossoms, which signify autumn and allude to the fourth-century scholar-official and poet Tao Qian, who wrote poems about the chrysanthemum and most famously a poem entitled "Peach Blossom Spring," about a utopian village removed from the turmoil of dynastic China. Tao was an exemplar of the merits of reclusion and self-cultivation.

The dish is heavily potted with well-levigated clay, but impurities have nevertheless created quite large pinholes through the glaze, particularly on the bottom. The thick glaze is glassy and of greenish tint. Fine sand adheres to the neatly finished foot and inside the foot ring. The glaze on the bottom has pooled above the foot ring.

1. The illustrations cited in Butz and Kawahara, *Chinesische Porzellane*, p. 72 and p. 90, no. 50, come from a 1710 reprint edition of the *Bazhong huapu*, published in Kyoto and now in the collection of the Berlin Museum for East Asian Art.

50. Dish

青花五彩鸳鸯莲纹方盘

Ming dynasty, ca. 1635–1645

Porcelain decorated in underglaze cobalt blue
and polychrome enamels

H. 2 cm; W. 9.5 cm

Sir Michael Butler

This unusually small square dish (Jp: *mukozuke*) would have been one of a set made for export to Japan. Its rim is decorated with a key fret border painted in underglaze cobalt blue. The center scene is painted in enamels only and depicts two ducks on opposite banks of a small waterway. A male mandarin duck struts beneath three very large lotus blossoms and a lotus pod. Near the opposite shore, by a lotus pad, his mate is swimming towards the drake.[1] In China, the mandarin duck (Ch: *yuanyang*) has symbolized marital happiness since the Tang dynasty (618–906). In Japan, the mandarin duck (Jp: *oshidori*) is also emblematic of a happy marriage; the two characters used to write the birds' names mean "male mandarin duck" and "female mandarin duck." In addition, a pair of ducks in Japan is used to connote "congratulations, or a wish for growing prominence because the Japanese word *oshidori* is a homophone for two words which mean 'take authority.'"[2] The lotus, so prominently placed

in the composition, is also a symbol of marriage. It is known in Chinese as *hehua* or *lianhua*; while *hua* simply means "flower," *he* is a homophone for "harmony" and *lian* is a homophone for "continuous." The presence of the lotus seed (Ch: *lianzi*) pod among the blossoms represents a wish for the prompt arrival of sons (Ch: *zi*).[3] In both China and Japan, the lotus depicted with mandarin ducks connotes a happy marriage as well as the well-being of one's progeny.[4]

The dish is covered with a glaze of notably blue-green tone; a few pinholes are visible, particularly on the corners of the dish on the back. Its foot ring is unglazed, beveled, and thinner than usual on this type of square dish. The bottom is glazed and bears an apocryphal six-character Chenghua (1465–1487) mark inscribed in underglaze blue in very attenuated characters.

1. I am indebted to Dr. Joseph Chang and Dr. Yu Hui for confirming the paired Mandarin ducks motif.
2. Baird, *Symbols of Japan*, p. 113.
3. Bartholomew, *Myths and Rebuses*, p. 7.
4. Baird, *Symbols of Japan*, p. 89.

51. Dish

青花梅纹圆盘

Ming dynasty, ca. 1630–1645
Porcelain decorated in underglaze cobalt blue
H. 3.5 cm; Diam. 21 cm
Butler Family Collection

This striking dish is decorated with blossoming prunus, or plum, arranged asymmetrically to cover most of the surface. Its angular branches convey the character of the prunus, blooming bravely despite the frost and snow of early spring. Two branches rise around the rim of the dish towards a swallow flying down between the two long boughs. One of the "three friends of winter," the prunus connotes tenacity and purity, or integrity.

The dish was thrown on a wheel; traces of the tool and probably the potter's hand are visible in the center, where the glaze has pooled in concentric circles. Its decoration was created in reserve, with the cobalt ground applied over a stencil of prunus and bird, and a few bare branches were added with a bamboo tool. The bird's wings were embellished with brushstrokes of cobalt pigment. Marks left by the potter's thumb and fingers as he glazed the dish can be seen on the left side of the dish near the rim. The back is covered with a thick glaze which has a blue-green tinge and prominent pinholes. Four large spots of cobalt and a few smaller splashes dot the back of the cavetto. The bottom is glazed, and masses of grey and brown kiln grit have stuck to the glaze inside and outside the crudely finished, shallow foot. A *fu*, "happiness," mark is inscribed on the bottom in seal script within two blue rectangles encircled by a single blue line.

52. Dish

五彩飞鸟纹圆盘

Ming dynasty, Chongzhen period (1628–1645)

Porcelain decorated in polychrome enamels

H. 2.8 cm; Diam. 15.5 cm

Butler Family Collection

Painted with enamels only, this dish is decorated with an extraordinarily abstract, almost ruffled, Lake Tai rock and bamboo shoots which spring from behind the rock. Above the bamboo, a flock of birds crosses the sky propelled by bands of iron-red clouds. Five of the birds are colored with green enamel and outlined in dark aubergine; five are yellow and outlined in iron red. The dish is covered in a thick glaze of greyish tone; the glaze on the bottom has a dull grey-blue cast and numerous pinholes. Its shallow, round foot ring is unglazed but much small kiln sand adheres to it. Under the dish, the glaze has pulled away from the inner circumference of the foot in a thin line, revealing a light orange body. Chatter marks are faintly visible on the slightly convex bottom. Circular tool marks can be seen around the underside of the dish; they were not smoothed in the potting process as they normally would have been on wares made for the domestic Chinese market. On the bottom, an apocryphal six-character Chenghua (1465–1487) mark in underglaze blue is surrounded by a single blue line.

53. Dish

青花五彩爵禄封侯纹盘

Ming dynasty, Chongzhen period (1628–1645)

Porcelain decorated in underglaze cobalt blue
   and polychrome enamels

H. 3 cm; Diam. 14.4 cm

Butler Family Collection

This twelve-sided dish, probably finished in a mold, reflects an elaborate production process despite the crude finish of the foot. It is decorated in a combination of underglaze blue and polychrome enamels requiring separate applications and two firings. The deer, the bird, the heads of the wasp and monkey, and the stems and leaves of the flowers on the rim are painted in underglaze blue, glazed, and fired at or above 1280° centigrade. Then the polychrome enamels would have been applied and fired at a much lower temperature. The delicacy of the deer's spots and the orchid's petals painted in iron red bespeak the hand of a skilled painter, despite the lack of depth in the composition and the mad angles of the ground line and diminutive pine. The decoration represents a Chinese rebus using homophones or similar-sounding words for bird (*que*), deer (*lu*), wasp (*feng*), and monkey (*hou*) to form the auspicious phrase *juelu fenghou*, "high rank and riches."[1] Painted on the rim are the orchid, the prunus, the peony, and perhaps the camellia.

   Chatter marks are faintly visible under the relatively white glaze on the bottom. Large chucks of kiln grit adhere to the bottom inside the unglazed foot. A blue line

encircles a square mark which in Chinese reads *tianxia taiping*, "great peace under heaven," in seal script. Impurities in the clay have caused two pinholes on the front of the dish, but otherwise the glaze and body are well bonded.

1. I am indebted to Terese Tse Bartholomew for this interpretation of the rebus. *Que* sounds like *jue*, a noble rank in China. Literally, the phrase means to "have the salary of a *jue* (knight), and to be conferred the rank of *hou* (marquis)."

54. Dish
青花骏马纹圆盘
Ming dynasty, ca. 1625–1635
Porcelain decorated in underglaze cobalt blue
H. 4 cm; Diam. 14 cm
Butler Family Collection

A small sun hangs over a scene typical of the late Ming dishes made for the Japanese market. Two frisky horses gallop at full speed, manes and tails flying, across a foreground indicated by a clump of grass. A hill and a long plateau from which a flag is waving in the breeze decorate the middle distance. Beyond the hill are a pagoda and another long plateau. In China the galloping horse is emblematic of speed and endurance and also symbolizes strength and courage.[1] In the Shinto religion of Japan, the horse was able to carry messages between heaven and earth.[2]

The rim of the dish has numerous small *mushikui*, "moth-eaten" edges. Two large pieces of black kiln grit pierce the glaze on the front of the dish. Both the foot and the slightly convex bottom are unglazed; it is highly unusual not to have a glazed bottom. The foot is hastily beveled, and coarse kiln grit adheres to the foot and the glaze outside the foot. On the underside of the dish are circular lines from the potter's fingers or a tool, put there while the bowl was still on the wheel. They were not smoothed away as they would have been on domestic wares. These circular lines characterize other examples of this ware that was made for the Japanese market in this period, including the blue-and-white dish decorated with two fighting cocks (cat. no. 63) and the dish painted with the deer, monkey, wasp, and bird (cat. no. 55).

1. Ong, *Chinese Animal Symbolisms*, p. 150.
2. Baird, *Symbols of Japan*, p. 144.

55. Dish
青花爵禄封侯纹圆盘
Ming dynasty, probably Chongzhen period
   (1628–1645)
Porcelain decorated in underglaze cobalt blue
H. 2.8 cm; Diam. 14.8 cm
Butler Family Collection

The dish has a crenellated border typical of many such small dishes made in this period for export to Japan.[1] Its decorative elements are completely out of scale: a wasp the size of a bird, a monkey the size of a deer. Here, a Chinese rebus expressing a wish for high rank and riches,

juelu fenghou, has been transformed by the demands of the Japanese market. The four elements of the rebus—bird (*que*), wasp (*feng*), monkey (*hou*), and deer (*lu*)—are arranged in a circle, and three of them seem poised for attack. The scene is framed asymmetrically by a pine, complete with vines hanging from the branches, and a bank of clouds atop the tree.

All the animals and other elements of the composition are outlined with more care than on earlier *kosometsuke* dishes. The deer is depicted with the requisite spots on its back, and graded washes are used in the landscape. But still the scene is rendered quickly and spontaneously. The foot ring reflects the speed of production which typifies wares for the Japanese market. Its unglazed foot is unevenly undercut and hardly beveled. Large bits of kiln grit adhere to the foot, inside and out. Chatter marks can be seen through the glaze on the bottom. Four flaming pearls adorn the reverse of the cavetto; a single blue line encircles the back of the dish outside the rim, and a double blue line outside the foot. The warping of the dish in firing, which makes it appear wider from top to bottom, adds to its careless charm.

1. See, for example, Butz and Kawahara, *Chinesische Porzellane des 17. Jahrhunderts für Japan*, nos. 5–9, 11, 19.

56 a–e. Set of five dishes

青花山君图套盘

Ming dynasty, ca. 1625–1635
Porcelain decorated in underglaze cobalt blue
H. 2.9–3.5 (range); Diam. 14.6–15.2 cm (range)
Lent by the Asian Art Museum; Effie B. Allison Collection, Gift of J.V. West and B.V. Gewald (B81P41–45)

These five dishes (Jp: *mukozuke*) illustrate the variations possible on individual dishes which make up a set produced for the Japanese market in the late Ming. They also demonstrate the humor and charm Jingdezhen potter-painters could bring to the depiction of a ferocious animal. Yoshiko Kakudo likened their depiction on these dishes to "a cartoon of a stretching kitten."[1] In China, the tiger is one of the four directional animals; it represents the West and is often paired with the dragon, symbol of the East. The tiger is also an attribute of Fenggan (Jp: Bukan), one of Chinese Buddhism's *sansheng*, or "saintly persons of unofficial status," and a friend of Han-shan (Jp: Kanzan) and Shide (Jp: Jittoku), all from Tiantai Mountain. The three were important Chan (Jp: Zen) Buddhist icons in China and Japan where, together with Fenggan's tiger, they were depicted as "The Four Sleepers."[2]

In China the tiger was also an attribute of Zhang Daoling who founded the Five Pecks of Rice (Ch: Wudoumi Dao), or Heavenly Master (Ch: Tianshi Dao), School of Daoism in Sichuan in the second century. By the Southern Song dynasty (1127–1279), Zhang was associated with the monastery at Longhu Shan (Dragon and Tiger Mountain), still one of religious Daoism's major sites today. Zhang was a noted alchemist and exorcist, and hence came to be depicted with the tiger, a symbol of exorcism.[3] In Japan, the use of a tiger as companion and mount derives from Chinese religious iconography. The tiger is king of beasts, the most ferocious animal but also the strongest and most courageous. In Japan, tigers also act as talismans to ward off demons and disease.[4]

The paintings on the dishes vary slightly; the pine is different on each, and the expressions on the tigers' faces vary from sleepy and flirty to canny. On three of the dishes, the ground plane on which the tiger stands defies all notions of spatial logic, and on one dish, the sun does not shine at all. All five dishes are covered with a thick glaze of greyish tint and are painted in broad brush strokes with a rather blue-black cobalt. All five have unglazed and undercut shallow foot rings, with chatter marks visible under the glaze on the bottoms. Four of the five dishes have relatively tidy foot rings with little kiln grit, but one dish has a foot ring with very large chunks of kiln grit. The backs of the dishes are decorated with double blue lines around the foot, a single blue line under the rim, and three pearls, each with four satellite dots surrounding them.

1. Kakudo, *The Effie B. Allison Collection*, p. 20.
2. See Jan Fontein and Money L. Hickman, *Zen Painting and Calligraphy* (Boston: Museum of Fine Arts, 1970), pp. xxix–xxx; nos. 3, 7, 29.
3. S. Marchant and Son, *Exhibition of Ming Blue and White Porcelains: the Drs. A. M. Sengers Collection* (London: Marchant and Son), p. 87.
4. Baird, *Symbols of Japan*, pp. 164–66.

57. Plate

青花鱼纹圆盘
Ming dynasty, ca. 1630–1645
Porcelain decorated in underglaze cobalt blue
H. 3 cm; Diam. 20.3 cm
Lent by the Asian Art Museum; Effie B. Allison Collection, Gift of J.V. West and B.V. Gewald (B81P4)

An amazingly abstract design surrounded by a seven-sided border decorates the center of this plate. A wavy sea occupies the foreground, and on the left a large tsunami wave appears about to engulf two fish with little pod feet flying over the sea. A sun disk hangs high in the sky, which is dominated on the left by a dark, intertwined bank of clouds which Yoshiko Kakudo likened to a dragon.[1] The plate is relatively well potted and covered with a thick glaze. Where the glaze has parted on the front of the dish, the body has fired red. The unglazed foot ring is sharply undercut, and chatter marks are visible under the glaze on the bottom. Kiln grit has stuck to the foot. A single blue line encircles the back of the rim, two blue lines surround the foot, and two abstract plants decorate the back of the cavetto.

1. Kakudo, *The Effie B. Allison Collection*, p. 27, no. 28.

58. Dish
青花英雄独立纹圆盘
Ming dynasty, ca. 1630–1645
Porcelain decorated in underglaze cobalt blue
H. 2.5 cm; Diam. 15.9 cm
Lent by the Asian Art Museum; Effie B. Allison
Collection, Gift of J.V. West and B.V. Gewald
(B81P40)

The noble falcon, depicted in three-quarter view, stands silhouetted against a plain ground. A rock on which it stands and two thin clouds under a tiny sun are the only suggestions of its surroundings. The potter-painter emphasized the bird's piercing eyesight, for which it was valued in China and Japan. Its posture accentuated the courage and aggressiveness which, by the Edo period (1615–1868), made the falcon a symbol of "the warrior class" in Japan.[1] The jagged edges of the border around the rim reflects the aggressive nature of the bird. In Chinese, the falcon (Ch: *ying*) is a homophone for "hero" (Ch: *yingxiong*). The image of the bird standing on one foot implies the expression *yingxiong duli*, "the independence of heroes."

This dish not only illustrates the austerity of many Japanese tea wares from Jingdezhen, a reflection of the aesthetic of early Edo Japan, but it also brilliantly illuminates the economy with which many were painted. Here, the rock was outlined with one thin stroke and squared off with another, and then the plant was outlined. Afterwards, the rock was washed with two strokes, one

dark and one medium blue, and four dots were used to fill in the petals beneath the bird. The bird was outlined with three or four strokes and then infilled with two tones of blue wash. Also quickly formed would have been the straight, shallow foot ring. No time was wasted removing the kiln grit that clung to the glaze on the bottom of the dish inside the foot.

1. Baird, *Symbols of Japan*, p. 109.

59. Dish
"福"字款五彩圆盘
Ming dynasty, ca. 1630–1645
Porcelain decorated in polychrome enamels
H. 2 cm; Diam. 14 cm
Butler Family Collection

This small molded dish with a foliated rim was part of a set of dishes (Jp: *mukozuke*) made solely for export to Japan. An angular pine and a large falcon atop a Lake Tai rock painted in aubergine enamels dominate the composition. The piercing green eye of the falcon bespeaks his iconographical role in China; the bird symbolized keen vision and valor.[1] In Edo Japan (1615–1868), "falcons and hawks became the natural emblems of the Japanese warrior class due to their keen eyesight, their predatory nature, and their boldness."[2] A small yellow bird with green wings hovers over the pine. Prunus leaves[3] sprout beside the rock and

bamboo grows beside the pine. Thus the dish is also decorated with the theme "three friends of winter" (the pine, prunus, and bamboo), which symbolizes attributes of the Chinese scholar: integrity, constancy, and purity. Eight *ruyi*, "wish-granting" symbols, hang from the scalloped border.

The dish has a small everted rim and is covered with a glaze of blue-green tone; there are small pinholes in the glaze. On the underside of the dish, the concentric marks made by the potter's tool when it was being turned on the wheel are visible under the glaze; they have not been smoothed out as they would have been on most dishes made for the Chinese market. The foot is shallow and hastily beveled, and there are a few bits of kiln grit and green glaze adhering to it. A mark reading *fu*, "happiness," is painted in seal script on the glazed bottom.

1. Ong, *Chinese Animal Symbolisms*, p. 287.
2. Baird, *Symbols of Japan*, p. 109.
3. Regina Krahl, "Plant Motifs of Chinese Porcelain: Examples from the Topkapi Saray Identified through the Bencao Gangmu," part 2, *Orientations* 18 (June 1987), p. 25.

60. Footed Dish
青花鹿纹支足盘
Ming dynasty, probably Tianqi period
   (1621–1627)
Porcelain decorated in underglaze
   cobalt blue
H. 5 cm; Diam. 18 cm
Butler Family Collection

This molded dish with scalloped rim rests on three stubby feet. It is decorated with two deer prancing on a promontory reached by bridges to the left and right. A grassy mound sits at the bottom of the foreground. The sun hangs in the sky on the left, and an insect plunges downward under an elongated cloud which hovers over the scene on the right. It is an auspicious design. The Chinese word for "deer," *lu*, is a homophone for "emolument," specifically the salary of an imperial official, and implies prosperity. The deer is also an attribute of Shou Lao, the Daoist god of immortality who is sometimes pictured holding a peach, another symbol of longevity, or a *ruyi* scepter, a wish-granting symbol emblematic of immortality.

The form of this dish is related to the molded lotus-form dish made for the Chinese domestic market in the end of the Wanli era, around 1600 to 1620, often decorated with a Chinese seal script character in the center and a six-character Wanli mark on the foot.[1] Whereas Wanli lotus dishes made for the Chinese are perfectly painted and potted, the adaptations made for the Japanese market in the following reigns are hastily potted and haphazardly painted. The petals on the underside of this dish resemble more those of a chrysanthemum than a lotus; the form of this dish is identical to another in the exhibition decorated with an elephant carrying the Buddhist aura (cat. no. 103).

The dish is heavily potted and painted in relatively light blue cobalt; the bodies of the deer and the two bridges are painted with graded washes. Its greyish glaze has a slight greenish tint. On the rim above the deer, cracks in the glaze reveal a white body, while the *mushikui* on the rim reveal the red of an iron-rich body. The back of the dish is incompletely glazed, and the glaze has pulled away from the recesses formed between the molded petals. Kiln grit adheres to the unglazed bottoms of the three feet.

1. Wang Qingzheng, *Qinghua youlihong* [Underglaze Blue and Red] (Shanghai: Shanghai Museum; Hong Kong: Woods Publishing Company, 1987), p. 107, colorplate 101.

61. Dish

青花鹿纹花口盘

Ming dynasty, probably Tianqi
    period (1621–1627)
Porcelain decorated in underglaze
    cobalt blue
H. 3 cm; Diam. 18 cm
Butler Family Collection

As on the previous dish (cat. no. 60), the outside of the cavetto is molded to resemble a chrysanthemum. Its form is reminiscent of the lotus shaped dishes made for the domestic Chinese market in the Wanli era, often with a Chinese character in seal script in the center.[1] This dish is decorated in the center with a scene containing two deer, a large pine, and bamboo sprouting at the base of the pine.

Like many wares made for the Japanese market in this period, the world depicted in the center of the dish is turned upside down; the dark deer which follows the piebald deer walks on an almost vertical ground plane, and the pine leans precipitously over both deer. A wispy but turbulent cloud hovers over the pine, and half the sun is obscured by the single blue line that frames the scene. The form and painting of the pine is also typical of the period; the tree has a twisted trunk, two writhing branches, and needles depicted in clumps of short dark lines covered with a medium blue wash. Both the pine and the deer are symbols of longevity; the word for "deer" in Chinese, *lu*, is also a homophone for the word meaning "emolument," the salary paid to an official, and thus its representation implies a wish for prosperity.

The dish is molded and covered with a thick greyish glaze. Long chatter marks are evident on the bottom. As on many wares of this period made for the Japanese market, kiln grit adheres to the glaze inside and outside the unglazed foot ring.

1. Wang Qingzheng, *Qinghua youlihong*, p. 107, colorplate 101.

62. Dish

青花松鹤同春纹圆盘

Ming dynasty, probably Chongzhen period
    (1628–1645)
Porcelain decorated in underglaze cobalt blue
H. 3.5 cm; Diam. 20 cm
Butler Family Collection

The image of the pine on this dish exemplifies the unselfconscious charm of imagery on Jingdezhen porcelains made for the Japanese market. The pine is depicted with particularly angular limbs and four round clumps of needles painted in short, dark lines and covered with circles of medium blue wash. Looking like eyes, two holes between the top branches and the center clump of needles animate the tree, which seems to be dancing with outstretched arms. Four swirling clouds further enliven the scene.

In China, the pine is a symbol of longevity, as is the crane which hovers above it; Shou Lao, the Daoist god of immortality is often depicted flying on a crane to meet the Eight Daoist Immortals. A crane and pine, when depicted together, "imply a wish for [a] bride and groom to live to a ripe old age"; the design is thus a general wish for longevity "known as *songhe tongchun* or *songhe xialing* and was an important Chinese wedding motif."[1] The deer is a symbol of immortality and is also paired with Shou Lao.

The dish is relatively carefully potted and covered with a greyish glaze; the glaze on the bottom inside the foot ring has a paler grey cast. Kiln grit adheres to the unglazed foot, and chatter marks can be seen under the glaze inside the foot. A thick blue line surrounds a six-character mark of the Chenghua reign (1465–1487); the characters are unusually heavily painted. The deeply undercut foot ring probably caused the center of the dish to drop so that an indentation is visible on the interior of the dish at the center of the pine.

1. Bartholomew, *Myths and Rebuses*, p. 16.

63. Dish

青花争雄斗志图圆盘

Ming dynasty, probably Chongzhen period
(1628–1645)
Porcelain decorated in underglaze cobalt blue
H. 3.5 cm; Diam. 16 cm
Butler Family Collection

This large dish with a high foot ring and an everted rim reflects a favorite theme in China and Japan, the cock fight (Ch: *douji* or *zhengxiong*). The cock, one of the twelve animals of both the Chinese and Japanese zodiac, represents *yang*, the male principle, and when depicted as a fighting cock, it signifies courage and the fighting spirit so valued in Japanese society.[1] This particular rendering depicts two cocks facing one another in an asymmetrical stance behind the grassy clumps in the foreground. An insect buzzes above the cocks, and distant mountains and a sun top the scene.

The dish is heavily potted on the bottom. There are several noticeable pinholes in the glazed interior. Where the glaze has separated on the reverse side of the cavetto, the body has fired a bright orange. The glazed bottom has three small firing cracks. Large pieces of kiln grit adhere to the glaze inside and outside the unglazed foot. There is a gold repair to the interior rim left of the mountain. Gold or red lacquer repairs are typically done in Japan.

1. Baird, *Symbols of Japan*, p. 104.

64. Dish

五彩爭雄斗志圖花口盤

Ming dynasty, ca. 1625–1635
Porcelain decorated in polychrome enamels
H. 2.4 cm; Diam. 13.2 cm
Butler Family Collection

This molded hexagonal dish with a lobed, brown-glazed rim is painted in enamels only. Its small size suggests that it was one of a set of five or ten dishes (Jp: *mukozuke*) used for the formal meal, *kaiseki,* that is part of the tea ceremony. In the center, two long-tailed phoenix cocks face each other in a most combative posture; phoenix cocks were especially popular in Japanese decorative arts and exemplify courage and a martial spirit.[1] The cocks face each other above a sprig of bamboo and two small garden rocks of yellow and green. Bamboo and a pine with aubergine trunk spring from behind the large Lake Tai rock beyond the cocks. The cavetto is decorated with three floral sprays, probably camellia, and three butterflies. In China and Japan, butterflies symbolize the souls

of the living and the dead as well as joy and longevity. This dish is related to a series of porcelains decorated with similar flowers, floral sprays, and butterflies and which includes a pair of bottles found in a Chinese tomb dated to 1628 and a single bottle in a tomb dated 1634.[2] The fighting cocks painted on this dish also decorate a blue-and-white dish in the exhibition (cat. no. 63).

The rim is warped and there are two lumps beneath the glaze on the underside of the cavetto. Impurities in the clay body have pierced the thick glaze, which is without tinge. The bottom of the dish reveals the speed of its manufacture. Clumps of kiln grit adhere to the glaze on the bottom, inside and outside the foot, which is unglazed and scarcely beveled. A deep blue mark reading *fu,* "happiness," in seal script is inscribed within a rectangle on the bottom.

1. Baird, *Symbols of Japan,* pp. 101, 104.
2. Suzanne Kotz, ed., *In Pursuit of the Dragon: Traditions and Transitions in Ming Ceramics, an Exhibition from the Idemitsu Museum of Art* (Seattle: Seattle Art Museum, 1988), p. 152 and pl. 85.

65. Dish

五彩冠上加冠纹圆盘

Ming dynasty, ca. 1635–1645
Porcelain decorated in polychrome enamels
H. 3 cm; Diam. 21 cm
Butler Family Collection

A few of these striking dishes survive in private and museum collections in the West and in Japan.[1] According to Yoshiko Kakudo, dishes of this size would have been made for the Japanese market and used to serve broiled fish and other relatively substantial foods.[2] Given the bright enamels used on this dish, it is difficult to imagine its use in the chaste tea ceremony practiced by the followers of Rikyū and Furuta Oribe. But because descriptions of seventeenth-century tea ceremonies are meagre, often we can only conjecture about usage.

The dish is decorated with an expansive cockscomb on a long stalk, flanked by chaste bamboo. Beside the giant plant, a hen and five of her six chicks are transfixed by a worm. A brilliantly delineated butterfly in iron-red and green enamels flies over the hen, and a wasp hovers over the cockscomb. The butterfly and wasp are embellishments supplied by the potter-painter. Otherwise, the scene is taken directly from *Caobenhua shipu* [Poems and Paintings of Flowering Plants], the sixth volume of an eight-volume compendium of the Tianqi era (1621–1627) entitled *Bazhong huapu* [Manual of Eight Painting Styles] (Jp: *Hasshu gafu*). The particular plate in question illustrates a poem entitled "Cockscomb."[3] The Chinese name for cockscomb is *jiguanhua* (lit., "chicken crown flower"); *guan* refers to a royal crown or the hat of an official in the emperor's civil service and at the same time is a homophone for a word meaning "government official." The comb on the hen coupled with the cockscomb flower forms the rebus *guanshang jia guan*, meaning "one official promotion after another" and the financial security implied by an official position.

The dish, which has a small everted rim, is light and carefully potted. Its shallow foot ring is unglazed and beveled. Because the thick grey-blue glaze was not carefully applied, considerable kiln grit has stuck to the foot, the glazed bottom, and the back of the cavetto. Specks of green glaze mar the back of the cavetto and the rim.

1. See Michael Butler et al., *Seventeenth-Century Porcelain from the Butler Family Collection* (Alexandria: Art Services International, 1990), p. 67, no. 29.
2. Kakudo, *The Effie B. Allison* Collection, p. 6.
3. Butz and Kawahara, *Chinesische Porzellane*, p. 74, no. 39.

IV. Chinese Scholars' Themes and Landscapes for the Japanese Market

66. Charcoal Container

青花山水人物纹炭钵

Ming dynasty, ca. 1625–1640

Porcelain decorated in underglaze cobalt blue

H. 9.8 cm; W. 12.4 cm

Lent by the Asian Art Museum; Effie B. Allison Collection, Gift of J.V. West and B.V. Gewald (B81P22)

Once filled with ash, this hexagonal charcoal container would have held a piece of burning charcoal with which to light a pipe. In Japan, tobacco became fashionable with tea devotees in the early seventeenth century. The host would place a tobacco tray (*tabako-bon*) holding pipes, a container for loose tobacco, and a charcoal container inside the waiting room for use before the tea ceremony.[1]

The sides of this container are decorated with six different landscapes, all of which derive from conventions of Chinese scholars' art. In one scene, a mounted Chinese scholar followed by a servant holding his furled parasol is depicted about to cross a bridge. Next, a fisherman in a boat poles past a prunus and a tall pine. In the third scene, a scholar and his servant sit on a promontory jutting out over water with a very vertical mountain in the distance. Then a large pine, symbol of the upright scholar, is depicted dominating a riverbank. The fifth side depicts a figure and a servant crossing a bridge and a third figure on an adja-

cent bridge carrying a long banner. And finally, a boatman poles toward land under a giant willow and a new moon. As Yoshiko Kakudo pointed out, the clouds in these landscapes are painted in a manner similar to that on certain Xuande period (1426–1435) blue-and-white porcelains decorated with swirling clouds and a pagoda or two, a type known in Japan as *Undode*. Sen no Rikyū (1522–1591), one of Japan's leading tea masters, was known to have possessed such a bowl, and they were extremely popular with later sixteenth-century tea masters.[2]

Like all the charcoal containers illustrated in Kawahara's *Ko-sometsuke*,[3] this charcoal burner is relatively heavily potted and the interior is glazed. It is made of poorly levigated clay; the thick glaze is full of pinholes and has pulled away from the edges at the bottom during firing to reveal the body which has fired a light orange. The cobalt has a blackish tone; the decoration is rendered primarily in dark outlines and washes. In its potting characteristics, this dish closely resembles the deep dish decorated with a landscape in the exhibition (cat. no. 81).

1. Sen, *Chanoyu: the Urasenke Tradition of Tea*, p. 57; see also Tanaka and Tanaka, *The Tea Ceremony*, p. 171 for an illustration of a tobacco tray.
2. Kakudo, *The Effie B. Allison Collection*, p. 10, Hayashiya and Trubner, *Chinese Ceramics from Japanese Collections*, p. 87, no. 46.
3. Kawahara, *Ko-sometsuke*, vol. 2, *Monochrome Section*, nos. 433–56.

67. Dish

五彩義之遺鵝圖方盤

Ming dynasty, ca. 1635–1645
Porcelain decorated in polychrome enamels
H. 2.5 cm; Diam. 13.6 cm
Butler Family Collection

This square dish with indented corners is one of a set of dishes (*mukozuke*) possibly made for the small meal, *kaiseki,* that formed part of the tea ceremony. The central panel is decorated with the figure of a Chinese scholar, probably Wang Xizhi (303–361), sitting under a pine with needles depicted in iron red and covered with circles of green enamel. Tendrils of moss trail from the pine, which is topped with clouds of iron red and an iron-red sun. Wang holds a peculiarly-shaped scalloped fan and sits beside a very tall slip case filled with volumes of books. A servant proffers him a small goose, whose neck Wang was reputed to have admired

for its S-curve. Wang Xizhi was China's most famous calligrapher, who held a gathering at the scenic Orchid Pavilion (Ch: Lanting) outside Shaoxing city in the year 353. Forty-two scholar-poets wrote poetry and drank wine from cups which floated by on lotus leaves. At the end of the poetry competition, Wang composed a preface to the poems and wrote it out in calligraphy of unsurpassed beauty, creating a masterpiece which became a model for calligraphers throughout Chinese history. He had also established the format for the Chinese literary gathering.

The dish has a brown-glazed rim and is covered with a thick and glassy, greyish glaze which has pulled away in a few spots to reveal the white paste of the body. A few large pinholes have burst through the glaze, and bits of green glaze dot the foot and the underside of the cavetto. The square unglazed foot is beveled, and the glazed bottom bears a *fu,* "happiness," mark written in underglaze blue in seal script within a blue double square.

68. Dish

五彩敦頤愛蓮圖六角盤

Ming dynasty, probably Chongzhen period
(1628–1645)
Porcelain decorated in polychrome enamels
H. 2 cm; Diam. 15 cm
Butler Family Collection

The hexagonal dish is decorated with a scene painted with only polychrome enamels. It depicts the figure of a scholar dressed in a soft cap and loose robes and seated in front of a balustrade gazing at a preternaturally large lotus in the water below. Behind him is a body of water, and in the distance are rocky ledges, pines, a leafless tree, and a flowering bush. A small sun shines at the top of the scene. The figure on the promontory is probably Zhou Dunyi (Zhou Maoshu; 1017–1073), China's first neo-Confucian cosmologist. Zhou combined Confucianism, with its elaborate theories of human nature and man's role in society, with concepts from early Chinese cosmology and religious Daoism to create one of the foundational works of neo-Confucianism, the *Diagram of the Great Ultimate* and its explanatory text.[1] Zhou Dunyi

also wrote a short essay, *In Praise of the Lotus,* which was recited by schoolboys throughout imperial China. The lotus had been the Buddhist symbol for purity because it rose through the mud to bloom clean and white. But thanks to Zhou's essay, the lotus also became the neo-Confucian "flower of purity and integrity" and thus the symbol of the Confucian "princely man."[2]

This dish, which was probably formed in a mold, is relatively carefully finished. It has a shallow cavetto and a wide, undecorated rim finished with brown glaze. The glaze is thick and of a pale-greenish tint. Impurities in the body have resulted in a few pinholes in the glaze. Tiny specks of green glaze cling to the outside and inside of the unglazed foot, which is carelessly finished. Chatter marks can be seen under the glaze on the bottom, which has a firing crack a half centimeter long and bears an underglaze-blue *fu,* "happiness," mark in seal script within a double square.

1. For more about Zhou Dunyi's contribution to neo-Confucianism, see Fung Yu-lan, *A History of Chinese Philosophy*, vol. 2 (Princeton: Princeton University Press, 1953), pp. 434–51.
2. Peter Valder, *The Garden Plants of China* (Portland, Oregon: Timber Press, 1999), p. 230.

69. Dish

青花五彩行旅图花口盘

Ming dynasty, ca. 1635–1645
Porcelain decorated in underglaze cobalt blue
  and polychrome enamels
H. 4 cm; Diam. 21 cm
Sir Michael Butler

This dish with a foliated and brown-glazed rim is decorated with scholarly motifs popular in Japan as well as China. It is decorated in the center with a generic scholar making his way through a landscape on a mule and followed by a servant carrying a parasol. The landscape is indicated by a pine cut by an iron-red cloud and a ground plane edged in green and punctuated by two green rocks. This scene is surrounded by a narrow, foliate border of six abstract patterns, three in iron red and three in underglaze blue; each underglaze-blue pattern has a counterpart in iron red. The rim is decorated with six panels. Three have lobed cartouches surrounded by abstract patterns in underglaze blue. The cartouches contain scenes of the scholar in seclusion: two scholars playing the Chinese game of *weiqi* (Jp: *go*) in the wilderness, a solitary fisherman, and a rider in a landscape. The three cartouches alternate with panels containing one of the "three friends of winter"—the pine, prunus, and bamboo—which in China and Japan connote the scholarly attributes of integrity, perseverance, and flexibility.

This sturdily-potted dish was probably finished on a mold. There are numerous pinholes on the underside of the dish; kiln sand and grit adhere to the shallow beveled foot, which is quite thick, as well as to the glaze outside the foot. The bottom is glazed, and there are a few small glaze cracks in the bluish-white glaze. It bears a square *fu*, "happiness," mark in cobalt-blue seal script.

70. Dish

五彩进士图方盘

Ming dynasty, ca. 1635–1645

Porcelain decorated in polychrome enamels

H. 2 cm; W. 9.5 cm

Butler Family Collection

This small, square dish with notched corners is decorated with the iconic figure of a Chinese scholar who has just achieved the dream of every parent during the Ming and Qing dynasties: he has been awarded first place in the Palace Examination and certified top scholar in the land by the emperor of China. Such a scholar would have passed three levels of extremely rigorous state examinations and received a *jinshi* degree, the rough equivalent of a Ph.D., before taking the Palace Examination. *Jinshi* degree-holders were the only males privileged to join the emperor's civil service, which administered the laws and governance of China. Their official salary would enable them to support their family and perhaps to buy land to enhance the family's prosperity.

The figure is depicted in a scholar's cap with its long hat strings, a formal robe, and a large belt. He holds a sprig of *Osmanthus fragrans* above his head and stands on an iron-red cloud. Both are symbols of his exalted achievement. At the top and bottom, the scholar's image is framed by an iron-red and green-enameled border of overlapping scales, and, at the sides, by interlocking hexagons in a pattern known in Japan as the six-sided turtle-shell motif, which occurs on Momoyama-period textiles and Oribe wares of the early seventeenth century.[1] Lotus blossoms decorate the four corners of the border. In a secular context, the lotus represents a wish for prosperity and, when paired with the image of the first-place scholar in the emperor's civil service examinations, represents the strongest possible wish for promotion and prosperity.

The dish is heavily potted; the paste is well levigated and quite white, with few imperfections. Its square foot ring is unglazed and neatly beveled. A square, underglaze cobalt-blue *fu*, "happiness," mark is inscribed in seal script on the glazed bottom. A dot of underglaze blue marks the reverse of the cavetto outside the foot.

1. Murase, *Turning Point*, nos. 74, 90.

71. Five Dishes
青花五彩山水人物纹套盘
Ming dynasty, ca. 1630–1640
Porcelain decorated in underglaze cobalt blue
    and polychrome enamels
H. 2 cm (approx.); Diam. 14 cm (approx.)
Sir Michael Butler

These five dishes are very different in feeling from the austere underglaze-blue *kosometsuke* wares of the Tianqi
period (1621–1627), but their offhand painting and potting exhibit a similar spontaneous quality. The scalloped
rims are finished with brown glaze and painted with two

cranes and two *ruyi*-shaped clouds in underglaze blue and
overglaze iron-red, yellow, green, and aubergine enamels. A different variation on a scholarly theme is painted
in the center of each. All the scenes take place in a landscape; two of them take place beneath a pine, which symbolizes the scholarly attributes of integrity and
perseverance. In one scene, two scholars are drinking
together. One holds out a cup in his right hand, while
holding a kettle in his left. Another kettle is keeping warm
next to a board for *weiqi* (Jp: *go*), sometimes referred to
as "encirclement chess," one of the four scholarly accomplishments in China and Japan.[1] Another dish is decorated with a scholar seated under a pine, contemplating

a wild chrysanthemum plant.[2] Two of the other scenes take place under a willow, which connotes spring; a seated sage is watching a child, the future scholar, at play. On the fifth dish, a boy is playing football, and a taller boy is carrying a leaf over his shoulder; the leaf alludes to the parasol carried over the adult scholar who has passed the imperial examinations and is thus eligible for a post in the emperor's civil service.

Four of the dishes have square marks reading *tianxia tai ping*, "great peace under heaven," in the most cursory seal script, and one has a *fu*, "happiness," mark in seal script. Because they are painted with different scenes and marks, the set may have been assembled in Japan. But all five dishes share the same form and similar potting characteristics. The dishes were finished in a square mold and have wide and elegant, thinly-potted rims. There are numerous firing cracks in the rather transparent glaze; where the glaze has pulled away, a light orange body is revealed. A very great deal of kiln grit adheres to all five foot rings, which are shallow and very quickly finished. The bottoms are glazed and the marks encircled by a single blue line. One of the dishes has a gold lacquer repair. The underglaze cobalt blue is quite deep and bright, and the copious use of iron red in the *ruyi*-shaped clouds, the cranes' wings, the cloud banks, and the scholars' robes gives these dishes an immediacy and "carry" that is unusual in wares of the late Ming made for the Japanese market.

1. Baird, *Symbols of Japan*, p. 289–90.
2. Regina Krahl, "Plant Motifs of Chinese Porcelain: Examples from the Topkapi Saray Identified through the *Bencao Gangmu*," part 1, *Orientations* 18 (May 1987), p. 63.

72. Dish

青花五彩山水人物纹盘
Ming dynasty, ca. 1630–1640
Porcelain decorated in underglaze cobalt blue
   and polychrome enamels
H. 3.5 cm; W. 17 cm
Butler Family Collection

This square dish with chamfered corners was painted and potted in the spontaneous, offhand manner valued by some Japanese of the late Ming. The brown-rimmed dish is decorated with a landscape organized in three distinct ground planes, one above the other, with the balance of the composition weighted to the right. A rocky shore in the foreground gives way to a literatus seated in a large blue boat propelled through the water by a servant. Rocks, mountains, and large flowers in underglaze blue and enamels make up the far distance. Tufts of aquatic grasses and lines of iron red are scattered about the middle ground in an attempt to describe recession and give movement to the water. A blue sun shines over the landscape.

The dish is heavily potted and luted together with slabs of clay which have warped in the firing, most notably the side of the dish at the bottom of the landscape. A firing crack is visible on the upper left inside the dish. The blue-tinged glaze has numerous pinholes on the front and base. Kiln grit adheres to the base, which has been smoothed with a rag and left unglazed except for streaks of brown glaze and flecks of green.

73. Dish

青花釉里红山水人物纹圆盘

Ming dynasty, ca. 1630–1645
Porcelain decorated in underglaze cobalt blue
    and copper red
H. 2.9 cm; Diam. 15.3 cm
Private Collection

The scene on this small dish is a Japanese version of a classic Chinese visual metaphor: the reclusive scholar as a lonely fisherman communing with nature. Here nature is portrayed in large unstructured rock formations rapidly outlined and filled in with dark, somewhat inky cobalt with light blue accents. The dark trunk of a tilting willow frames the side of the scene; its branches hang over the fisherman and a promontory where a large tree peony with copper red blossoms sprouts at a mad angle. Water and sky meet in the undecorated center space of the dish. A flock of tiny birds fly towards the sky, and four preternaturally large carp with jaunty fins and tails fly away

from the fisherman. The arrangement of dark masses on either side of the scene and the copper red of the peony and fish accentuate the asymmetry of the decoration and add to the whimsy and charm of this dish.

This dish would have been one of a set of five or ten. Dishes of cobalt blue with copper red like the three in this exhibition (cat. no. 38, 73, 74) may well have come from the same kiln; the potting characteristics are very similar. A number with these designs survive in various sizes.[1] This dish has an everted rim and a shallow, undercut foot. It is made of relatively well-levigated clay and covered in a thick glaze of blue-green tint. Globs of kiln grit adhere to the glaze outside the foot, and chatter marks are visible all around the glazed bottom inside the foot. The back is decorated with four pearls, each surrounded by four dark blue dots.

1. See, for example, Kilburn, *Transitional Wares and Their Forerunners*, p. 164, no. 127; and Butz and Kawahara, *Chinesische Porzellane*, no. 10a–e, for a set of five, each with a wide rim decorated with grapes, vines, and butterflies.

74. Dish

青花釉里红山水人物纹圆盘

Ming dynasty, ca. 1625–1640
Porcelain decorated in underglaze cobalt blue
    and copper red
H. 3.5 cm; Diam. 21 cm
Butler Family Collection

This dish is painted with a crenellated border and a scene of a mounted scholar, hat strings flapping in the breeze, followed by his servant carrying a furled parasol. They approach a multi-storied city gate and a city wall with crenellated battlements. A huge banner, accented in copper red and standing on a battlement, flaps in the breeze. Two clouds outlined in copper red hang in the sky, and a red sun shines down upon the scene. On seventeenth-century Chinese porcelains made for the domestic market, the servant is almost always depicted carrying the scholar's *qin*, a "seven-stringed horizontal zither" which

members of the scholar-gentry regarded as a prized possession.[1] The ability to play the *qin* was regarded as one of the "four gentlemanly (or scholarly) accomplishments" in China. On most porcelains made for export to Japan in this exhibition, the scholar and/or his servant carry a parasol.

All the elements of this scene are outlined with the most cursory strokes and filled in with dark washes laid down quickly and imprecisely. The dish is heavily potted and covered with a glaze of blue-green cast full of impurities. Pinholes pierce the glaze in front and particularly on the convex bottom, where chatter marks are also visible. The glaze on the bottom has pulled away from the foot. The shallow foot ring is undercut carefully beveled, and very large clumps of kiln grit are stuck to the glaze all around it. The back of the cavetto is decorated with four pearls each surrounded by four small dark dots.

1. Baird, *Symbols of Japan*, p. 283.

75. Dish

青花山水人物纹圆盘

Ming dynasty, Tianqi period (1621–1627)
Porcelain decorated in underglaze cobalt blue
H. 2.4 cm; Diam. 15.9 cm
Lent by the Asian Art Museum; Effie B. Allison
 Collection, Gift of J.V. West and B.V. Gewald
 (B81P37)

This small dish has a wide rim decorated with three different repeating motifs: auspicious abstract symbols representing the Buddha's earrings, rhinoceros horns, and a loosely rendered *yin-yang* symbol, or "comma" design (Jp: *tomoe*).[1] The center of the dish is painted with a landscape. In the foreground, a scholar mounted on a mule is followed by a servant carrying a furled parasol. The branches of a deciduous tree lead the eye to hills, an unrealistically large hut, and pine trees in the far distance. Figures and landscape elements are outlined in dark cobalt with quickly drawn strokes and filled in with very rapidly applied washes of dark and medium blue. The dish shares potting characteristics with two other dishes in the exhibition, both of which have a wide rim decorated with asymmetrically placed rondels and a four-character Tianqi (1621–1627) mark in regular script (cat. nos. 33, 34). Except for the

unglazed foot ring, which is shallow and encrusted with kiln grit, the dish is covered in a glaze of marked blue-green cast. The back of this dish is undecorated.

1. Baird, *Symbols of Japan*, p. 218. I am indebted to Terese Tse Bartholomew for identifying the earrings and rhinoceros horns.

76. Dish

天啟款青花商山四皓圖圓盤

Ming dynasty, Tianqi mark and period
 (1621–1627)
Porcelain decorated in underglaze cobalt blue
H. 4.5 cm; Diam. 20.4 cm
Butler Family Collection

This dish is one of the few in the exhibition that depicts what could be classified as a narrative theme, which in Chinese art usually focuses on figures from history, literature, legend, or religion whose actions were exemplary. The four scholars depicted ambling in a mountainous wilderness probably represent the Four Greybeards, or Hoaryheads, of the Shang Mountains (Ch: Shangshan *sihao*; Jp: Shozan *shiko*). In the middle distance, a willow with a knot in its truck hangs over the figures, and a mountain and sun loom in the far distance. This is also one of relatively few dishes inscribed with a four-character Tianqi mark that depict more than two figures. The composition of the painted scene is typical of wares of the 1620s made for the Japanese market; nothing is on the same ground plane as anything else.

The Four Greybeards were white-haired sages who withdrew to the mountains at the end of the Qin dynasty to avoid the chaos of the times. They refused the invitation of the new Han emperor, Gaozu (reigned 206–195 BCE), to serve as officials at his court because the new emperor favored the use of force and disdained the advice of scholars. But they did appear at court in support of Liu Ying, Gaozu's elder son and heir-designate, after Gaozu decided to name a new heir, the eleven-year-old son of a favorite concubine. When the emperor asked why they came in support of his son after refusing his summons, they are alleged to have answered in part, "We have heard that the heir-designate is humane and filial, and is respectful of scholars; in the empire there are none who would not

stretch out their necks, willing to die for the heir-designate. Thus did we your servants come."[1] Gaozu was so impressed with their commitment that he retained Liu Ying as heir apparent. The Four Greybeards became exemplars of courageous political conduct, risking their lives by their original refusal to serve and by their eventual support of a worthy emperor-designate. According to Alan Berkowitz, the fame of the four sages soon spread from their ranking as Confucian exemplars to their incorporation "into literature, alchemic lore, organized religion, local traditions and decorative art." And their fame spread geographically as well. Kendall Brown has demonstrated that the Four Greybeards were one of the most pervasive themes in Japanese painting created for Buddhist monks, the aristocracy, and the military of the late sixteenth to seventeenth centuries.[2]

The dish is relatively well potted and the front covered with a glaze that has no tinge and few pinholes; the rim has a few *mushikui*. Its back is painted with three pearls, each surrounded with three dark blue dots, and is covered with a glaze of blue-green tint. The bottom is glazed and bears a four-character mark reading *Tianqi nian zhi*, "made in the reign of Tianqi," surrounded by two thick blue circles. The shallow foot ring is undercut, and there are a few clumps of kiln grit clinging to the glaze inside the foot.

1. Quoted from the *Shiji* by Sima Qian in Alan J. Berkowitz, *Patterns of Disengagement: The Practice and Portrayal of Reclusion in Early Medieval China* (Stanford: Stanford University Press, 2000), pp. 65–67.
2. Ibid., pp. 79–80; Kendall H. Brown, *The Politics of Reclusion: Painting and Power in Momoyama Japan* (Honolulu: University of Hawaii Press, 1997), pp. 4–5.

77. Dish

青花桐下婴戏图圆盘

Ming dynasty, ca. 1625–1635
Porcelain decorated in underglaze cobalt blue
H. 3.5 cm; Diam. 20.4 cm
Butler Family Collection

This large, shallow dish is decorated with an unusual scene: seven boys playing blind man's bluff, three in shirts and trousers, four naked. They are playing in a garden setting framed by grassy knolls in the foreground, a tree on the left, and clouds on the right. One of the naked boys hides behind the trunk of the *wutong* tree; by the Ming dynasty, this tree was often associated with the "Hundred Children" motif. The boys represent the hundred sons of King Wu, founder of the Zhou dynasty (ca. 1050–256 BCE). During the Song period (late 11th–mid 12th c.), their depiction had come to signify a wish for numerous progeny to carry on the ancestral sacrifices and continue the family lineage. By the Chenghua period (1465–1487) of the Ming dynasty, King Wu's sons also came to personify *guizi*, or "noble sons," who finished first in their examinations and could therefore become officials in the emperor's civil service. Their imperial salaries would guarantee the prosperity and continuity of the family.[1] In addition, the sun above the *wutong* tree suggests the auspicious phrase *xuri dongsheng*, "the sun rising in the eastern sky," connoting youthful vigor.

The dish is painted with blackish-blue cobalt and covered with a greenish glaze; the glaze on the bottom is greyer than that on the rest of the dish. There are two large *mushikui* and a small gold repair on the slightly everted rim. Where the glaze has separated from the body on the outside of the foot, an iron-rich, bright orange body is revealed. The unglazed rounded foot is shallow and hastily beveled, and large bits of kiln grit cling to the glaze in patches inside and outside the foot. The underside of the cavetto bears circular traces of the potter's fingers or a tool, left while the dish was being raised on the potter's wheel.

1. Terese Bartholomew, "One Hundred Children: From Boys at Play to Icons of Good Fortune," in Ann Barrott Wicks, ed., *Children in Chinese Art* (Honolulu: University of Hawaii Press, 2002), pp. 57–83.

78. Plate

青花百子图圆盘

Ming dynasty, ca. 1625–1635
Porcelain decorated in underglaze cobalt blue
H. 4.1 cm; Diam. 24.7 cm
Lent by the Asian Art Museum,
    Gift of Roy Leventritt (B69P83L)

This heavily-potted and crudely-painted plate shares potting characteristics and decorative techniques with another dish in the exhibition, decorated with an elephant holding a lotus in its trunk (cat. no. 104). The figures in the center of both plates are starkly depicted against a plain ground. On this plate, a lady has picked a branch of an early-blossoming fruit tree, possibly the apricot tree. The apricot blooms in the second month of the Chinese year and thus became the floral symbol of the second month, corresponding approximately to March on the Western calendar. The white apricot is sometimes referred to in Chinese as *bai guozi* "one hundred fruit," or as *bai guozhi*, "the hundred fruit branch,"[1] and is thus a rebus for *baizi*, "the hundred boys," which had become "icons of good fortune" by the late Ming.[2] On this plate, the lady who picked the flowering branch is giving it to a second woman. Six of the "hundred boys" play beside her, so the dish could possibly represent a wish for many sons.

98

This plate shares all the physical characteristics treasured by Japanese tea devotees. The plate is very heavily, even clumsily, potted. Its rim has numerous *mushikui*, and the glaze has flaked off near the junction between rim and dish. The thick glaze is of blue-green tint and replete with countless pinholes. The plate was coated so quickly that the glaze barely covers the plate in places; it has pulled away in numerous spots revealing a dark orange, poorly levigated body. The unglazed foot ring is very thick and dotted with bits of black kiln grit, which have stuck to the center of the dish as well.

The tree and figures were painted in blue-black cobalt with great speed and some assurance but without subtlety. A flat dark wash was used to fill in the garments, leaving only gestures and the position of the bodies to suggest three dimensionality and movement. The five blue lines which decorate the rim underscore the austerity of the center scene and guaranteed that no Chinese consumer would give it a second glance. Yet this plate, echoing many characteristics of earlier Japanese stoneware, has been highly valued in Japan for nearly four hundred years.[3]

1. Eberhard, *A Dictionary of Chinese Symbols*, p.21.
2. Bartholomew, "One Hundred Children," pp. 57–83.
3. Stephen Little correctly ascribed the origin of the rim decoration to Oribe wares; Little, "*Ko-sometsuke*," p. 14. See also Murase, *Turning Point*, p. 93, no. 32, for a picture of shards from an Oribe plate and a bowl with similar rim decoration.

79. Dish
青花山水纹扇形盘
Ming dynasty, ca. 1630–1645
Porcelain decorated in underglaze cobalt blue
H. 7 cm; W. 16 cm; D. 18.5 cm
Butler Family Collection

This dish (Jp: *mukozuke*) in the form of a folding fan was part of a set of five made for the Japanese market.[1] The open fan shape is unusual. Fan-shaped *mukozuke* are usually narrow, the fan only slightly unfolded. The upper part of this fan is decorated with a mountainous

landscape outlined in fine lines and filled in carefully with medium and dark washes. It depicts a mountain pass; high cliffs enclose the scene, which includes a body of water, a rocky promontory, two boats, and two huts. A man walks behind a horse or donkey, which may or may not be pulling a plow. The branches of two leafless trees lead the eye into the distance, to a small settlement, perhaps a temple complex, tucked into the notch in the high mountains.

The dish was formed from a sheet of clay. A bottom slab would have been cut and then three narrow strips luted to the sides to form the fan. Impurities in the body, which was not too carefully levigated, have caused numerous pinholes in the front and back of the dish. It is covered with a thick glaze of blue-green cast, much of which flaked off as the dish cooled after firing. Little glaze remains around the rim, on the bottom at the lute joint, and on the bottom and inside of the knob which holds the fan together. The bottom is glazed and has three stubby feet with unglazed bottoms. The sides are decorated with the tasseled lozenge, a "precious object," flanked by a peony and a *ruyi*-shaped cloud.

1. See Baird, *Symbols of Japan*, p. 250, for the significance of the folding fan.

80. Dish

青花山水人物纹菊口盘

Ming dynasty, ca. 1625–1635
Porcelain decorated in underglaze cobalt blue
Diam. 19.1 cm
Lent by the Asian Art Museum,
   Gift of Roy Leventritt (B69P93L)

This dish is molded in the form of a chrysanthemum, like two others in the exhibition (cat. nos. 60, 103). While the landscape in the center of the dish would have pleased less affluent Chinese buyers, the form of the dish, with its three stubby feet, would not have served a useful purpose in the course of a Chinese meal; it was too big to sit on small Chinese serving tables. In comparison with most wares produced by the Chinese for the Japanese market, however, this dish represents a considerable investment of labor. The rim is particularly intricate: each petal outlined in dark blue, infilled with light blue, and a darker blue half-moon added around a small white petal in reserve. There is an additional raised rim around the landscape.

The landscape resembles those on Wanli-era dishes of about 1600 to 1620; it was probably executed by potter-painters who worked for a kiln that produced export wares. A river intersects the land masses at almost a 45 degree angle. A house sits on promontory in the center while a novel bank of ruffled clouds with dark blue centers hovers on the left; a servant and scholar who came by boat approach the house. In the middle distance are rocky cliffs and a hut perched on a promontory. A small flock of birds leads the eye to distant mountains, dominated by one conspicuously perpendicular peak, and to another flock of birds. The contrast between the white ground of the river and areas painted in dark and medium blue washes is striking.

The dish is covered with a thick glaze of conspicuously blue-green cast, which has adhered well to the back unlike the glaze on another chrysanthemum-form dish in the exhibition (cat. no. 103). On the back, the glaze has pooled in the indentation between the back and the rim. A few large chucks of kiln grit are stuck to the bottom, and in only a few places, the glaze has pulled away slightly from the crevices between the petals. The bottoms of the three feet are unglazed.

81. Bowl

青花山水人物纹碗

Ming dynasty, ca. 1630–1645
Porcelain decorated in underglaze cobalt blue
H. 6.3 cm; Diam. 17 cm
Private Collection

The shape of this wide-rimmed, deep bowl is based on a Shino ware prototype;[1] nothing like this heavily-potted form was produced for any other domestic or export market besides Japan. Its square rim has notched corners and is decorated at the corners with a willow, a pine, bamboo, and perhaps the most bizarre lotus on any seventeenth-century porcelain.[2] Twisting, twirling vines spring from the lotus. The landscape in the bowl is equally bizarre, full of heavy dots (Ch: *dian*), a convention used for centuries by Chinese painters to contour mountains and hills. All the rocks and mountains except two in the far distance are covered with these dots. The components of the entire scene are outlined in dark and medium blue brushstrokes: the trees, the house, and the scholar and his servant on the foreground promontory awaiting the arrival of the boat nearing the shore. The rest of the landscape objects are filled in with medium and light blue washes. Only the boat and boatman escape the crude dark outlines used in most of the scene. The cobalt pigment is a dull, dark blue.

The bowl and rim are extremely heavy, made of badly levigated grey clay, and covered with a thick glaze of blue-grey tint. Large black pinholes pierce the glaze on the front and back. The wide foot ring is deep and beveled on the outside. A streak of light blue wash mars the back of the dish over the cavetto. The foot is encircled by two thick blue lines. Bits of kiln grit cling to the back. This porcelain serving bowl recreates the feel, if not the decoration, of a stoneware vessel more effectively than almost any other porcelain in the exhibition.

1. See Murase, *Turning Point*, p. 96, no. 35, near the bottom right corner of the illustration for a shard of a Shino ware prototype of the form. See also the "Shino serving dish" in Ryōji Kuroda and Takeshi Murayama, *Classic Stoneware of Japan: Shino and Oribe*, trans. Robert N. Huey and Lynne E. Riggs (Tokyo: Kodansha International, 2002), p. 64, picture 31.
2. See Bartholomew, "Botanical Motifs in Chinese Furniture," fig. 14, for the motif of pendant lotus and leaves under the seat of the throne.

82. Dish

青花山水人物纹莲口盘

Ming dynasty, ca. 1620–1630
Porcelain decorated in underglaze cobalt blue
H. 6 cm; Diam. 19 cm
Butler Family Collection

The lotus blossom form of this dish is based on a prototype made in the reign of the Wanli emperor (1573–1620) for the domestic market in China; it was carefully glazed and decorated with a large character in the center.[1] Here, however, the dish is decorated with a landscape. The mountains are depicted using the convention of repeating the outlines of peaks one on top of the other to suggest depth and mass. In the foreground, two scholars chat under a willow tree; one of them gestures towards the scenery. A group of houses is sheltered under nearby boulders. The middle ground, demarcated by two boats and a distant shoreline, is occupied by a promontory with a pavilion and trees and numerous wondrously contoured mountains topped with leafless trees.

The back of the dish is molded with two rows of petals. In China and Japan, the lotus is the Buddhist symbol of purity; the flower blooms pure and clean after rising through the mud and water. The smaller row of petals is decorated with the auspicious swastika emblem alternating with a pearl surrounded by four dark blue dots. The twelve larger petals are painted with floral sprays alternating with five Buddhist symbols—the endless knot, the wheel of the law, the parasol, the pair of fishes, and the conch shell—and the lozenge, one of the eight precious objects.

The dish is heavily potted of well-levigated clay and covered with a bluish-white glaze. Its deep foot ring has been cut off, cleaned, and beveled on the outside. The glazed bottom is painted with concentric blue circles and has no mark. A small firing crack cuts across the circles.

1. See, for example, Wang Qingzheng, *Qinghua youlihong*, p. 107, no. 101.

83. Dish

青花松树纹莲口盘

Ming dynasty, ca. 1620–1630
Porcelain decorated in underglaze cobalt blue
H. 3.8 cm; Diam. 20.2 cm
Private Collection

This dish, molded in the form of a lotus, was produced for the Japanese market in the 1620s. A classic *kosome-tsuke* pine decorates the center of the dish. The pine is depicted with gnarled trunk, twisted branches, clumps of dark blue needles covered with a medium blue wash, and vines trailing from its branches. In China and Japan, the pine is a symbol of longevity. The pine is also associated with the ideal attributes of a Chinese scholar: constancy and integrity. It is forever green, and in winter the pine does not sully itself by permitting its branches to touch the earth, even when weighted with snow.

The pine is surrounded by three borders of scalloped lines and three tiers of lotus petals, all densely decorated with a wide variety of Buddhist and Daoist symbols. The lotus itself is a Buddhist symbol of purity. The symbols in the petal-shaped cartouches are randomly placed. They include an immortal with a staff standing on a sacred mountain, Lake Tai rocks with pine branches, a lone pine, sea grasses, and mountainous rocks (possibly Penglai, the Isle of the Immortals) under the Three Terraces constellation.[1]

84. Dish

青花山水纹莲口盘

Ming dynasty, ca. 1625–1635
Porcelain decorated in underglaze cobalt blue
H. 5.1 cm; Diam. 22.5 cm
Lent by the Asian Art Museum,
  Gift of Roy Leventritt (B69P113L)

This lotus-shaped dish is based on a domestic prototype, carefully potted and painted with bright blue cobalt, often with a seal script character in the center.[1] The dish from the Leventritt Collection is directly related to these earlier lotus dishes but is very different in character. It was made in a slightly more complicated mold than was the previous lotus dish in the exhibition (cat. no. 83). Both dishes in the exhibition were created for the Japanese market and painted with the quick, broad brushwork characteristic of earlier *kosometsuke* wares produced for the Japanese market.

The center of the dish is decorated with a landscape, slightly more up to date stylistically than some other landscapes in the exhibition. A large rocky cliff in the near distance shelters the boat with a lonely fisherman. A hut sits atop a promontory, and a pine with twisted trunk draws the eye back to a heavy rock formation in the far distance. The potter-painter has used graded washes on the rock formations, even if rather crudely done, to indicate recession. Around the landscape is a row of lotus buds, followed by a row of larger petals separated by small, pointed petal tips painted with Buddhist swastikas.

Waves spawning seaweed, waves with a lozenge surrounded by four pearls, and waves emanating an aura serve as Daoist symbols of transformation.[2] A few cartouches contain branches of prunus and peony. A final row of petals is decorated with the swastika, an auspicious Buddhist emblem in China and Japan. The many small petals filled with these symbols, often flanked by banks of clouds on either side, create an extremely busy visual effect.

The design elements are outlined with dark blue lines and filled in with a very quickly applied medium blue wash. A relatively bright cobalt pigment is used. On the back, two rows of petals are decorated with swastikas; the large row of petals above the foot ring is painted with medium blue wash and striations to indicate a rounded contour. The dish is heavily potted and covered with a thick bluish glaze which has not adhered perfectly to the indentations between petals on the back of the dish. Its deep foot ring is unglazed and beveled and has a line of kiln grit on the inside. A small firing flaw protrudes from within the double circle which decorates the glazed bottom.

1. See cat. no. 91 for information on the Three Terraces, *san tai*, constellation.
2. Little, *Taoism and the Arts of China*, p. 371.

The outer row of petals are decorated with a variety of plant motifs, all different, including a *lingzhi* fungus, a peach, pomegranate, sea grasses, peony, and chrysanthemum. On the reverse, the foot is surrounded by a painted border of lotus buds, and larger lotus-bud-shaped petals molded in relief are decorated with *ruyi* motifs alternating with swastikas.

The foot ring is unglazed and has fired a dark grey. The body is relatively well levigated but a good many pinholes have popped through the glazed bottom, which is decorated with two blue concentric circles but no mark. Kiln grit adheres to the glaze inside the foot and on the foot, which is unglazed and slightly warped in two places. The cobalt used to decorate the dish is quite a bright blue, and the thick glaze has a bluish tone, which slightly relieves the weightiness of the dish's form and decoration.

1. See for example, Wang Qingzheng, *Qinghua youlihong*, p. 107, no. 101.

85. Lobed Dish
青花岁寒三友图花口盘
Ming dynasty, ca. 1625–1635
Porcelain decorated in underglaze cobalt blue
H. 3 cm; Diam. 21 cm
Private Collection

This five-lobed dish with a crenellated border is decorated with the "three friends of winter": pine, prunus, and bamboo. According to Terese Tse Bartholomew, "this motif reigns supreme among the botanical motifs of China."[1] On this dish, the pine dominates the composition; it is by far the most imposing pine in the exhibition. It has five twisted branches, a long trunk with a knot on the lower section, and vines hanging from the branches. The nodes of the bamboo are delineated, while the leaves are brushed in quickly without outline; the prunus is depicted in an abstract, nonchalant manner. These three friends

symbolize noble attributes. The pine and bamboo remain green throughout the winter, thus connoting immutability and persistence. Braving the ice and even snow of early spring, the prunus blooms first among deciduous fruit trees. And because the bamboo bends in the wind but does not break, poets came to refer to it as *junzi*, "this gentleman."[2] Resistance to the elements has long been admired in China. This association insured that by the Ming dynasty, "the three friends of winter" would symbolize the idealized characteristics of a scholar-official: constancy, integrity, and flexibility.

This dish is heavily potted and covered in a thick bluish glaze. The cobalt on the front is slightly blue-black; the blue on the back is somewhat livelier. On the back of the dish, the five lobes are delineated; each is decorated with a pearl surrounded by four small dots. The bottom is glazed and painted with two concentric circles but no mark. The thick foot ring is beveled and contains a firing crack. Kiln grit clings to the foot ring and inside the foot, and a streak of grit has stuck to the glaze on the bottom.

1. Bartholomew, "Botanical Motifs in Chinese Furniture," p. 45.
2. Julia B. Curtis, *Chinese Porcelains of the Seventeenth Century: Landscapes, Scholars' Motifs and Narratives* (New York: China Institute, 1995), p. 161.

86. Plate

青花棕树纹圆盘

Ming dynasty, ca. 1630–1645
Porcelain decorated in underglaze cobalt blue
H. 3.5 cm; Diam. 21.3 cm
Lent by the Asian Art Museum; Effie B. Allison Collection, Gift of J.V. West and B.V. Gewald (B81P12)

The decoration in the center of this plate evinces the flat, two-dimensional composition typical of many *kosometsuke* wares of the 1630s and early 1640s. Two novel, gravity-defying objects have been added to a landscape. The three hemp palms (Jp: *shuro*) appear firmly rooted to the ground plane, but on the right, a pine-bark lozenge (Jp: *matsukawahishi*) decorated with a Buddhist swastika floats through the air.[1] A large rectangular object decorated with three lozenges, which may well be a Buddhist scripture, looms above one of the hemp pines. The book is depicted two-dimensionally with the spine on the same plane as the cover.

The whole scene probably has Buddhist connotations; hemp palms were often seen planted in "the small recesses of temples" in southern China, according to T. Samson, who was writing about horticulture in China and Japan in the 1860s.[2] The palms were introduced to

the West from Japan but are native to southern China. Three flying cranes, symbols of longevity, decorate the rim, interspersed with three butterflies (Jp: *chōchō*), which also symbolize longevity as well as the souls of the living and the dead in China and Japan.[3]

The plate is well potted, and its relatively refined glaze has adhered well to the body. Its foot ring was carefully trimmed. Chatter marks are visible under the glaze on the bottom.

1. Kakudo, *The Effie B. Allison Collection*, p. 29.
2. Quoted in Valder, *The Garden Plants of China*, p. 325.
3. Baird, *Symbols of Japan*, p. 101.

87. Plate
青花岁寒三友图圆盘
Ming dynasty, ca. 1630–1645
Porcelain decorated in underglaze cobalt blue
H. 3.5 cm; Diam. 22.2 cm
Lent by the Asian Art Museum; Effie B. Allison
  Collection, Gift of J.V. West and B.V. Gewald
  (B81P5)

This plate is decorated with a pine, a prunus, and a bamboo (Jp: *shōchikubai*). They are the "three friends of

winter" or "three friends of the cold season" (Ch: *suihan sanyou*) because they resist the rigors of the season. The pine does not sully its branches to touch the earth even when they are weighted with snow; the prunus, or plum, braves the wind and frost to bloom before any other deciduous tree; and the bamboo is flexible but does not break even in high wind. The pine and bamboo remain green throughout the winter. Thus they also came to represent the virtues of the upright scholar: perseverance, courage, and integrity. On this plate, the three friends are depicted as separate design elements. Hanging above the plum and bamboo, the pine is painted with gnarled branches and dark bunches of needles covered with medium blue wash. The plum is depicted in a very abstract manner typical of *kosometsuke* wares, with five branches of buds and one preternaturally large blossom emanating from a curved stalk. Sharing the same groundline with the prunus, the bamboo culms (stalks) are carefully delineated with nodes but the leaves are sparse and crudely painted. The cavetto is decorated with four peony blossoms and the rim with a border of chevrons. On the back, two blue lines encircle the foot and a single blue line surrounds the underside of the rim. The back of the cavetto is decorated with three *lingzhi* fungus heads.

The plate is more thinly potted than the few plates

in the exhibition dating definitely to the 1620s (cat. nos. 33, 34, 75). It is covered with a glaze of blue-green tint pierced with small pinholes. Small bits of grit mar the center of the plate, and chatter marks are visible on the glazed bottom. The glaze has pulled away inside the unglazed foot ring to reveal an orange body.

88. Plate

青花竹筏纹圆盘

Ming dynasty, ca. 1630–1640
Porcelain decorated in underglaze cobalt blue
H. 2.8 cm; Diam. 21 cm
Lent by the Asian Art Museum; Effie B. Allison Collection, Gift of J.V. West and B.V. Gewald (B81P8)

This plate is decorated with one of the most intriguing decorative schemes in the entire exhibition: six bamboo rafts. In the center of the plate, a bamboo raft is disintegrating in the rapid current of the river. The angles of the four bamboo logs detached from the raft and the coils of the loosened ropes which bound them create a powerful sense of the force causing the disintegration. The five intact rafts which decorate the rim are asymmetrically placed. They are tethered together by a long rope, whose undulations around the rim accentuate the urgency of movement conveyed in the center of the dish.

Bamboo rafts are still used in China today to move people and goods and to transport large bamboo logs from their source to construction sites. But the bamboo rafts on the plate represent a Japanese motif. As Merrily Baird observed, rafts (Jp: *ikada*) became popular in the decorative arts in the Momoyama and Edo periods (1573–1868), usually with cherry blossoms (Jp: *sakura*) or maple leaves (Jp: *momiji*) scattered on them. Cherry blossoms in particular were paired with running water, streams, and waterfalls, or with man-made objects, like rafts, associated with running water.[1] On this plate, the Chinese potter-painter has omitted the flowers or leaves, but the meaning, with its Buddhist implications, is unchanged: the ephemeral nature of life. The fragility of cherry blossoms connotes impermanence; therefore, they were

not generally used in Japanese family crests, despite the popularity of the blossom. Likewise, the maple leaf, associated with autumn, is quintessentially mutable, although, with its magnificent colors, the maple has remained a popular motif in painting and the decorative arts and was celebrated in poetry second only to the cherry blossom.[2] So the disintegrating raft, even without its usual iconographical compliment, speaks to us of the transience of worldly existence.

The back of the plate is almost as curious as the front. It is carved out at the center of the bottom and furnished with an unglazed wide rim which it might have sat on. But the potter also provided the plate with three very short feet beside the unglazed rim. A simple blue line and an undulating line with twelve loose scallops below it decorate the back of the plate just under the rim. Four cherry blossoms decorate the back of the cavetto.

The plate is more heavily potted than others in the Allison collection. It has a grey body and a thick glaze of bluish-grey tone; the glaze around two thirds of the cavetto is visibly cracked. Kiln grit adheres to the center of the bottom, which is glazed and has a firing crack.

1. Baird, *Symbols of Japan*, pp. 48–50, 266.
2. Ibid., p. 54.

V. DAOIST AND BUDDHIST THEMES ON PORCELAINS FOR THE JAPANESE MARKET

89. Dish

青花五彩仙人图圆盘

Ming dynasty, Tianqi period (1621–1627)

Porcelain decorated in underglaze cobalt blue and enamels

H. 3.3 cm; Diam. 16 cm

Butler Family Collection

This dish is decorated with the figure of an immortal standing on a cloud which is hastily outlined in iron-red, black, and green enamels. Three sprays of green leaves surround the cloud. The immortal is dressed in a loose

robe tied with a sash over a white shirt and loose white trousers. Behind his left shoulder is another cloud with a leafy branch emerging from one side. His left arm is raised, and the tail of a cloud appears behind it. Wisps of red and green clouds convey a celestial atmosphere, as does the flaming pearl with green tails above his right shoulder and the yellow cloud above his head. The immortal may represent the Rain Master, Yushi, a popular Chinese god often pictured with the Lord of Thunder, the Earl of Wind, and the Mother of Lightning. The Rain Master usually holds a cup of rain as well as his branch, which he dips into the cup and then sprinkles over the earth.[1] This small dish is one of a group of dishes made for the tea ceremony and decorated with figures painted in underglaze blue, often embellished with thickly applied enamels and four-character Tianqi marks. They are all spontaneously painted with pinwheel clouds and flaming pearls in improbable colors.[2]

On the underside, two blue lines encircle the dish below the rim and outside the foot. The bottom is decorated on either side of the foot with two sprays of foliage bearing six red berries. There are some kiln sand and dark bits of kiln grit stuck to the unglazed foot. The bottom is glazed, but in spots the glaze has pulled away from the side of the foot revealing a light orange body. A vigorously painted four-character Tianqi mark is inscribed on the bottom and encircled by two thick blue lines.

1. Little, *Taoism and the Arts of China*, pp. 238–39.
2. See for example, Butler et al., *Seventeenth-Century Chinese Porcelain*, p. 57; Butz and Kawahara, *Chinesische Porzellane*, p. 59.

90. Dish

青花刘海戏蟾图方盘

Ming dynasty, ca. 1630–1640
Porcelain decorated in underglaze cobalt blue
H. 4.1 cm; W. 16.5 cm; D. 17.8 cm
Lent by the Asian Art Museum,
    Gift of Roy Leventritt (B69P94L)

In the painting on this square dish with chamfered corners, a corpulent man wearing a dark cape and skirt hustles through a rocky landscape with shrubs and a willow, clutching a toad in his arms. His stomach protrudes over his skirt, and his open mouth and gait testify to the effort of catching and carrying the huge toad. The figure represents Liu Haichan, or Liu Hai, a Daoist adept who had served the Jin emperor in the year 911. During his tenure at court, Liu was visited by a Daoist master who initiated him into the mysteries of Inner Alchemy. As the master spoke, he constructed a pyramid of ten eggs and ten coins. He then pointed out that the precariousness of Liu's life as a courtier was far greater than that of the pyramid of eggs and coins. Consequently, Liu abandoned the court to become a hermit.[1]

Liu Haichan's principal attribute, a three-legged toad, is depicted with a string of cash protruding from its mouth. In popular folklore, Liu used this string of cash to lure the toad out of its hole in the ground, a feat which accounts for his nickname Haichanzi, or "Master Sea Toad." Ironically, although Liu Haichan abandoned worldly fortune and became famous as a master of Inner Alchemy, his association with this tale transformed him in the popular mind into an auspicious figure associated with money-making. He was sometimes included as one of the Eight Daoist Immortals and portrayed with the saintly Buddhist monk-poets Hanshan (Jp: Kanzan) and Shide (Jp: Jittoku) (see cat. no. 97).[2] Given Liu's appearance on numerous *kosome-tsuke* dishes, Liu Haichan, who was known in Japan as Gama Sennin, must have appealed to the Japanese sense of the peculiar.[3]

This dish is one of the few in the exhibition that appears deliberately warped: the sides of the dish above and below the figure are particularly indented. Warping would have devalued the piece in the eyes of the Chinese consumer, but to the Japanese such imperfections only added value to the spontaneity of the painting. A few splashes of glaze and chunks of kiln grit adhere to each corner of the unglazed base. Numerous firing cracks cut across the base, which is slightly convex; it had probably warped during firing. Sprays of bamboo and twigs decorate the four sides of the dish. The lip, which bears several *mushikui*, is covered with a pale blue wash above a darker line.

1. Little, *Taoism and the Arts of China*, p. 330.
2. Wen C. Fong and James C.Y. Watt, *Possessing the Past: Treasures from the National Palace Museum*, Taipei (New York: Harry N. Abrams, 1996), p. 346, pl. 167.
3. Kawahara, *Kosometsuke*, vol. 2, *Monochrome Section*, pp. 70, 84, 145.

91. Dish

青花五老观画图方盘

Ming dynasty, ca. 1635–1645
Porcelain decorated in underglaze cobalt blue
H. 3.2 cm; W. 13.5 cm
Private Collection

This warped little dish represents an aesthetic contrary to modern concepts of austere Japanese tea taste, but its intensely decorated surface and production flaws indicate that it was destined for Japan. Figures of the Five Ancients in the garb of Chinese sages decorate the center of the dish. The Five Ancients are the embodiment of the Five Elements (Ch: *wu xing*): earth, fire, water, metal, and wood. The Five Elements compose all earthly and heavenly phenomena and are kept in cosmic balance by the opposing forces of *yin* and *yang*. These two forces together form the Daoist "Supreme Ultimate" (Ch: *taiji*),

at once the sign of the unity of the Dao and of its duality: male and female, hot and cold, light and dark, hard and soft, dry and wet, heaven and earth.[1]

Four of the Five Ancients gaze fixedly at a handscroll which two of the sages hold up; one sage, wearing a square hat, faces the viewer. This handscroll depicts the Three Terraces (Ch: *san tai*), a constellation of six stars which Daoists believe regulates human affairs. The first of the Three Terraces represents the Emperor and Empress, gives life, and governs longevity. The second Terrace represents male nobles and their consorts, provides sustenance, and governs ancestral affairs. The third level represents the common people, provides protection, and governs military affairs.[2]

The imagery on this dish is as complex as its iconography. Its five figures are depicted with intricate brushwork; facial features, posture, and costumes are individualized. Two pines hang over them; in this con-

110

text, the pine is a symbol of longevity, as is the deer standing beside the stooped figure who holds up one end of the hanging scroll. The Five Ancients stand in a walled garden which opens onto a body of water; there are ships' masts in the distance and sun and clouds in the sky. Four lotus blooms, each with a *ruyi*, or "wish-granting," symbol on either side, decorate the indented corners of the square rim. The areas between the lotuses on the rim, above and below the center scene, are filled by a pattern of interlinked petals, and to either side of the scene, with a linked swastika pattern.

The dish is covered with a very thick glaze with many pinholes and long *mushikui*. There are small white lumps under the glaze on the back. The low, hastily beveled square foot is stuck on askew, and an indecipherable underglaze-blue mark is enclosed within a double square on the glazed bottom.

1. Little, *Taoism and the Arts of China*, p. 131; Peter Valder, *The Garden Plants of China*, pp. 441–42.
2. Personal communication with Shawn Eichman. See also John Lagerwey, *Taoist Ritual in Chinese Society and History* (New York: Macmillan Publishing Company, 1987), p. 54.

92. Dish

青花临流仙人图圆盘

Ming dynasty, ca. 1635–1645
Porcelain decorated in underglaze cobalt blue
Diam. 19 cm
Butler Family Collection

This is one of three dishes of similar decoration illustrated in the principal catalogue of *kosometsuke* wares by Masahiko Kawahara.[1] It depicts six figures in a curious configuration which must represent a "story" involving three of the Eight Daoist Immortals. The three male immortals can be identified by their attributes. Han Xiangzi, reputed to be the nephew of the Tang dynasty poet Han Yu, is depicted playing his flute. Lan Caihe, the slightly "unbalanced" immortal, holds a flower basket above his head. Zhang Guolao, sporting a beard and a square hat, raises his right hand as if to perform some feat of magic for which he was famed. Zhang was a Daoist "technique master" (Ch: *fangshi*); he folded his mule to the size of a wallet when it was not being used to carry Zhang through the countryside.[2]

The male immortals stand on the right behind two small hills, and below them, apparently in a stream or river, is a lady submerged to her waist. Two other ladies stand behind two hillocks overlooking the water; two boats propelled by oarsmen navigate the current. A pine stretches its branches across the top of the composition and a small sun beams down on the immortals and ladies. A second incarnation of the scene illustrated in Kawahara's book depicts four immortals in a group to the right of the three ladies. The utter lack of perspective in the scene, the improbable placement of the figures, and the inconsistent scale between the figures and the boats would have rendered the dish unacceptable to all but the Japanese at the time.

The dish is well potted of fine white clay with few pinholes. Both the border design and central figures are hastily painted with imprecisely applied graded washes, and the cobalt is a relatively lively blue. The foot bears three very dark prominent patches of grit and numerous smaller impurities, and sand clings to the carefully beveled foot ring. On the back, two blue lines surround the foot and a single blue line decorates the underside of the rim.

1. Kawahara, *Ko-sometsuke*, vol. 2, *Monochrome Section*, p. 148.
2. Little, *Taoism and the Arts of China*, p. 321; Kwok Man Ho and Joanne O'Brian, *The Eight Immortals of Daoism: Legends of Popular Daoism* (New York: Meridian Books, 1991), pp. 26–30.

111

93. Plate

青花五彩仙人图圆盘

Ming dynasty, ca. 1630–1635

Porcelain decorated in underglaze cobalt blue
and polychrome enamels

H. 2 cm; Diam. 20 cm

Butler Family Collection

This striking plate depicts a fisherman offering a fish to a sage. The rim of the dish is decorated with four floral sprays—hibiscus, peony, aster, and possibly camellia—in separate panels set off against a checkerboard pattern. Much of the central composition is filled with decorative elements, but the careful application of the cobalt pigment and enamels effect a tranquil scene. The head, arms, hands, feet, and legs of the figures are painted in underglaze blue, as are the cliffs, promontory, and some of the rocks that surround the sage. A cloud outlined in iron-red cuts off the branches of a willow with an aubergine trunk and reveals above it the very top of a green-roofed celestial building; a small iron-red sun hangs below.

The scene represents an episode in the hagiography

of Lü Dongbin (Jp: Ryotohin), one of the Eight Daoist Immortals. Lü's sword, Green Snake (Ch: Qingshe), which enabled him to combat evil and perform magic, is strapped to his back behind his loose robe. This scene may depict Lü's attempt to convert a fishmonger named Sun to religious Daoism, or it could represent his conversion of a fisherman named Yang Liu. Lü Dongbin's conversions of Sun and Yang Liu are described in his various hagiographies.[1] The best single visual source of scenes from Lü's life and legends is the murals in a building in the Yonglegong (Palace of Eternal Joy), a Daoist temple complex of the fourteenth century in Shanxi province. Mural no. YLG 20, on the eastern half of the north wall, illustrates a man holding a fishing pole with one fish attached and bowing to Lü Dongbin. A barefoot man with a black mustache and beard, wearing a green robe and white trousers like those of the fisherman on the plate, introduces the bowing figure to Lü Dongbin.[2] Unfortunately, the cartouche in the Yonglegong which would have identified the fishmonger or fisherman has been destroyed.

The plate is quite finely potted but impurities in the body have caused several black pinholes to pierce the relatively refined glaze of bluish tone on the front and back. The unglazed foot is carelessly beveled; two-thirds is covered with a thick coating of kiln grit. An apocryphal Chenghua (1465–1487) six-character mark was hastily written in the center of the glazed bottom and is surrounded by two blue lines.

1. These conversions are described in an article by Wang Chang'an in *Wenwu*, no. 8 (1963), pp. 66–78, and in the Song dynasty text *Yijian zhi* [Record of the Listener and Recorder] (1157–1202), by Hong Mai, cited in Paul R. Katz, *Images of the Immortal: The Cult of Lü Dongbin at the Palace of Eternal Joy* (Honolulu: University of Hawaii Press, 1999), pp. 214–15, 263, 291.

2. The scene from the Yongle temple is illustrated in Liao Ping, ed., *The Yongle Palace Murals* (Beijing: Foreign Languages Press, 1985), p. 86.

94. Dish

青花八卦纹八角盘

Ming dynasty, ca. 1625–1635
Porcelain decorated in under-
    glaze cobalt blue
H. 2.8 cm; Diam. 19.5 cm
Butler Family Collection

This octagonal dish is an intriguing combination of popular religion and Daoism. The transformation of Daoism as it traveled from China to Japan is a particularly complex tale; Chinese folk beliefs as well as facets of Daoism were absorbed into Japan through Esoteric Buddhism in the eighth through tenth centuries.[1] Depicted in the center scene is a hare holding a *lingzhi*, the immortality-granting fungus, in its mouth. The hare also symbolizes longevity and was often used to decorate porcelains made for the Chinese domestic market in the late Wanli era, around 1595 to 1620. But the image of the iconic hare on this dish was transmogrified by the destination of the dish. The hare, outlined in a few strokes, sits on a crudely rendered ground plane of dark wash flanked by wispy grasses. Way overhead, asymmetrically placed to the left, is a pine, also a symbol of longevity. The pine is painted with clumps of needles covered by dark blobs of cobalt wash and with vines trailing down from the branches. The placement of the rabbit and pine, the large blank space between them, the lack of realistic scale (a giant rabbit or a tiny pine), and the crude rendering of both typify Jingdezhen wares of the 1620s and 1630s made for the Japanese market.

The cavetto and rim of the dish are divided into eight panels; each panel is decorated with one of the Eight Trigrams (Ch: *bagua*), which are the basis of an ancient Chinese tradition of divining the future and understanding the cosmos. An important part of Chinese intellectual and religious life as early as the Western Zhou dynasty (ca. 1050–771 BCE), this method of divination from the *Yijing* [Book of Changes] became a critical component of the practice of alchemy in religious Daoism in the Six Dynasties period (220–589 CE) and later. In their search for immortality, Daoists used the Trigrams to explore the transformation of *yin* and *yang* in their elixirs of lead and mercury, a mixture which virtually ensured the demise of

many of its practitioners.[2] On this dish, the Trigrams are almost reduced to a decorative device; the *kan* Trigram is missing, the *li* Trigram is repeated twice, and the sequence does not follow either of the two conventional arrangements.[3]

On the front, the rim of the dish is decorated with a scrolling vine pattern. Three *lingzhi* fungus heads decorate the back of the dish. The foot and rim are encircled by a single blue line.

The dish is painted with blue-black cobalt and covered with a grey-green glaze. Long chatter marks are visible under the glaze on the bottom, which is painted with a blue double-line circle. There is considerable kiln grit adhering to the unglazed foot, which is very hastily finished and painted with a blue double line.

1. See Masuo Shin'ichiro, "Daoism in Japan," in Livia Kohn, ed., *Daoism Handbook* (Leiden: Koninklijke Brill, 2000), pp. 821–38, for a lucid summary of Japanese Daoism.
2. For an explanation of the Trigrams and the origin of religious Daoism, see Little, *Taoism and the Arts of China*, pp. 13–21, 139.
3. See Little, *Taoism and the Arts of China*, p.139, for more on the Fu Xi and Wenwang arrangements of the Eight Trigrams.

95. Plate

青花玉兔纹圆盘

Ming dynasty, ca. 1625–1635
Porcelain decorated in underglaze cobalt blue
H. 2.8 cm; Diam. 20.6 cm
Lent by the Asian Art Museum; Effie B. Allison
   Collection, Gift of J.V. West and B.V. Gewald
   (B81P11)

The motif on this plate is one of the most popular transmitted to Japan on *kosometsuke* wares from Jingdezhen; the Jade Hare appears frequently on surviving examples of Arita ware.[1] A symbol of immortality, the hare was an attribute of Chang'e, who became an immortal by stealing a pill containing the elixir of immortality and was banished to the moon as punishment for her theft. The chill on the moon caused Chang'e to cough up the coating on the pill, which turned into a hare as white as the whitest jade. This hare was often depicted beside Chang'e on the terrace of the moon palace pounding the elixir of immortality with a mortar and pestle. The hare is outlined in a few sure strokes, with fine light brushstrokes on his back, belly, and ears to convey a sense of volume. A rectangle with the characters *yu tu,* "Jade Hare," floats some distance above the hare.

The ground around the hare is decorated with *fukizumi,* or *soufflé* blue. Wax would have covered the body of the hare and the rectangle when the cobalt was blown onto the plate. The rim is decorated with five floral sprays, probably crabapple. Floral scrolls decorate the back. The plate is relatively well potted and covered on the top and bottom with a bluish glaze. There is kiln sand and grit around the unglazed foot ring. Two blue lines encircle the foot, and a single line is painted under the rim.

1. Kakudo, *The Effie B. Allison Collection,* p. 26.

96. Dish

青花五老观画图圆盘

Ming dynasty, ca. 1630–1640
Porcelain decorated in underglaze cobalt blue
H. 4 cm; Diam. 20.5 cm
Butler Family Collection

The figures of five aged men decorate the dish; three are holding bent staffs and two are holding opposite ends of a hanging scroll. All five have rounded shoulders and exaggerated craniums. They gaze intently at the *Taiji tu,* the Daoist diagram of the Supreme Ultimate, on the hanging scroll. The five men represent the Five Ancients, who stand for the Five Elements (Ch: *wu xing*): earth, water, fire, metal, and wood. These Five Elements constitute the basic material fabric of the Daoist universe and are kept in shifting balance by the cycle of *yin* and *yang,* the two opposing forces of the universe at the core of the Daoist "view of the structure of reality, the duality of phenomenal existence,"[1] manifested in female and male, cold and hot, dark and light, wet and dry, soft and hard, earth and heaven, and so on.[2] The *taiji* diagram encompasses the *yin* and *yang* and represents the unity of the Dao. The diagonal placement of the five bony men holding angular staffs against a large plain ground creates a striking asymmetrical design which would have appealed to Japanese sensibilities.

The dish is quite carefully potted of fairly well-levigated clay. Its bottom is undercut and has numerous pinholes; chatter marks are visible under the glaze. Several of the horizontal and down-strokes which form the six-character Chenghua mark on the bottom are drawn with considerable panache; the mark is surrounded by a single blue line. Grit and sand adhere to the bottom and inside of the unglazed foot.

1. Little, *Taoism and the Arts of China*, p. 131.
2. Valder, *The Garden Plants of China*, pp. 41–42.

97. Dish
青花刘海戏蟾图方盘
Ming dynasty, ca. 1635–1645
Porcelain decorated in underglaze cobalt blue
H. 4.1 cm; W. 18.1 cm; D. 18.1 cm
Lent by the Asian Art Museum; Effie B. Allison Collection, Gift of J.V. West and B.V. Gewald (B81P13)

This square dish with indented corners would have been part of a set of five dishes (Jp: *mukozuke*) made for the Japanese market. It is decorated with the figures of four immortals depicted with unusual care for *kosometsuke* ware. The figures are outlined with many thin brush-strokes, while the contours of their clothing are carefully delineated and outlined in modulated washes to indicate contour and movement. This brushwork reflects, albeit remotely, earlier techniques of Chinese figure painting on silk and paper. Similar but more refined painting can be found on countless pots made for the domestic Chinese market between 1630 and 1645 and decorated with narrative themes.[1] The figures on this dish represent two Buddhists of particular interest to the Japanese, Hanshan (Jp: Kanzan) and Shide (Jp: Jittoku), Tang Buddhist monks who wrote poetry.[2] They stand in front of two Daoist immortals. At the left rear, Liu Hai or Liu Haichan (Jp: Gama Sennin) is

shown using golden cash to bait the three-legged toad, who earned Liu his place as an auspicious figure associated with money-making. On the right, Li Tieguai (Jp: Tekkai) is leaning on his crutch, watching Liu Hai and his toad with considerable amusement. Hanshan holds his attribute, a scroll. Shide, identified by his broom, turns towards Hanshan but points with his right hand to Liu Hai and the toad.

Typical of Jingdezhen wares of the 1630s made for export and domestic markets, the corners of the cavetto are decorated with elaborate tassels and the rim is decorated in reserve with a molded border of lotus and tendrils on a blue ground. The dish is heavily potted of well-levigated clay with some pinholes. The glaze has a grey-blue tint, and the glazed bottom has numerous pinholes. Random bits of kiln grit cling to the square, beveled foot.

1. See, for example, Curtis, *Chinese Porcelains of the Seventeenth Century*, nos. 34, 40, 41, 54, 61.
2. See cat. no. 98, for more details about the two monks.

98. Plate

青花指日高陞图圆盘

Ming dynasty, ca. 1625–1630

Porcelain decorated in underglaze cobalt blue

H. 3.3 cm; Diam. 21 cm

Private Collection

The wide rim of this plate is decorated with a checker-board pattern found on plates made for Japan in the late 1620s and 1630s. Depicted in the center is the figure of a man holding a broom in his left hand and pointing with his right hand at the sun, which hovers above his finger. Two columns of calligraphy hang beneath the sun. The four characters in the right column read *zhi ri gao sheng*, "pointing at the rising sun," which in Chinese is a metaphor meaning "may you soon be promoted [in the emperor's civil service]." The left column reads *Bifeng ti*, "inscribed by Bifeng (Green Mountain)." Clouds swirl

above the figure's head, and the grassy mounds beneath his feet suggest a natural setting. He is flanked by two fences which resemble the prows of boats; garden rocks are depicted behind the fences.

The figure on the plate is Shide (Jp: Jittoku), a "saintly person in the 'unofficial status category'" of Chan Buddhist hagiographies.[1] Shide, who lived in the Tang dynasty, was a foundling adopted by monks at the Guojing Monastery in the Tiantai Mountains. There he worked in the kitchen; hence his attribute, the broom. He became the intimate of Hanshan (Jp: Kanzan), a monk, recluse, and poet who lived on Cold Mountain (Ch: Han-shan), also in the Tiantai Mountains. On Ming paintings and porcelains, the two friends were depicted with shaggy hair, "laughing or with smiles of saintly delirium," and clothed in tattered monks' robes. Both monks wrote poetry; the importance of Buddhism to their poems made the two "Chan eccentrics" popular figures in Japan as well as in China.[2] But allusions to Daoism in their poetry and the intermingling of Buddhism and Daoism led Han-shan and Shide to acquire Daoist attributes, such as the magical double-gourd on Shide's belt.[3]

The plate is relatively carefully potted, painted with washes of cobalt pigment, and covered with a blue-green glaze with only a few firing cracks. Its wide rim has an upturned lip and is encircled on the underside by a single blue line; the rim has numerous *mushikui*. Two clumps of barren branches sprout on opposite sides of the foot. Only a little kiln grit adheres to the carefully beveled foot ring, which is decorated with a blue double line border. Chatter marks are visible on the glazed bottom.

1. Marsha Weidner, ed., Latter *Days of the Law: Images of Chinese Buddhism*, 850–1850 (Lawrence, Kans.: Spencer Museum of Art, the University of Kansas; Honolulu, Hawaii: University of Hawaii Press, 1994), p. 189.
2. Burton Watson, "Introduction," in *Cold Mountain: 100 Poems by the Tang Poet Han-shan*, trans. by Burton Watson (New York: Columbia University Press, 1970), pp. 10–11; Baird, *Symbols of Japan*, p. 179.
3. Weidner, *Latter Days of the Law*, p. 390.

99. Dish

五彩参禅罗汉图菱形盘
Ming dynasty, ca. 1630–1645
Porcelain decorated in polychrome enamels
H. 3 cm; W. 18.3 cm; D. 14.4 cm
Private Collection

This lozenge-shaped dish and the quatrefoil dish in the exhibition (cat. no. 100) use identical decorative schemes in different formats. Both *mukozuke* are decorated in enamels only and depict the figure of a lohan (Ch: *luohan*; Jp: *rakan*) seated on a mat; a book sits on his bent right leg, hidden under his aubergine robe. The lohan's left hand rests on his raised knee, and he is seated on a green spotted mat with an aubergine border and iron-red fringe. He is portrayed against a patterned ground of rectangles, triangles, pentagons, and hexagons outlined in very dark brown enamel and painted in iron-red, yellow, green, and aubergine enamels, with some shapes left in unglazed white. This design, known as "cracked-ice motif," (Ch: *binglie wen*; Jp: *hyoretsumon*, *hyochikumon*), is also used

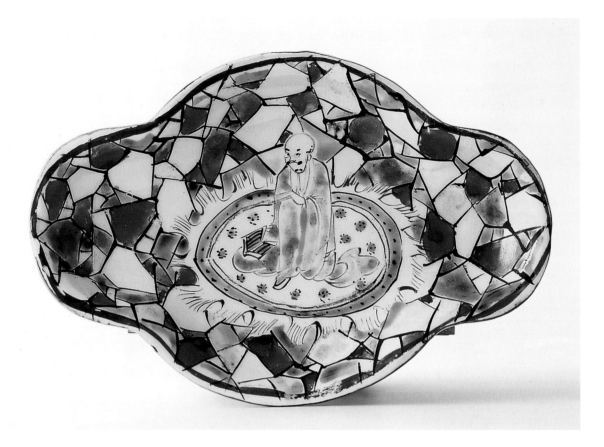

as a border pattern for prints.[1] It is sometimes referred to as the "stone wall" pattern by Chinese porcelain scholars.[2] The use of this background in polychrome enamels is most unusual; it was almost always used to decorate porcelains painted in underglaze blue.

The lohan depicted is probably Kanaka Bharadvaja (Jp: Hatsura Tasha), whose attributes include a book as well as a fly whisk.[3] He has a shaved head, bushy eyebrows, mustache, and unshaven chin. It is the same figure as on the quatrefoil dish from the Butler Family Collection (cat. no. 100). The two dishes were undoubtedly produced in the same kiln and are examples of the same design used on different shapes of mukozuke.

The dish is very heavily potted of clay containing many impurities. It is covered with a very thick grey glaze and has several small firing cracks on the bottom. The rim is covered with a brown glaze, which did not prevent glaze from flaking off after firing and leaving a few *mushikui* on the rim. Like the lohan quatrefoil dish, the rectangular foot ring was symmetrically placed on the bottom and neatly beveled. A lozenge-shaped mark written in dull cobalt and reading *da tang*, "great hall," in rapidly executed seal script sits in the center of the glazed bottom.

1. Baird, *Symbols of Japan*, p. 31
2. Michael Butler et al., *Shunzhi Porcelains: Treasures of an Unknown Reign* (Alexandria, Virginia: Art Services International, 2002), p. 123.
3. Baird, *Symbols of Japan*, p. 192.

100. Dish
五彩参禅罗汉图花口盘
Ming dynasty, ca. 1630–1340
Porcelain decorated in polychrome enamels
L. 18.5 cm; W. 12 cm
Butler Family Collection

This quatrefoil dish decorated with polychrome enamels is part of a set of identical dishes (Jp: *mukozuke*) which would have been used for the *kaiseki*, the small meal in the Japanese tea ceremony. Like the lozenge-shaped dish in the exhibition (cat. no. 99), this dish is decorated with a lohan (Ch: *luohan*; Jp: *rakan*) seated on a mat with a book by his side. His right knee is raised, and he holds an iron-red fly whisk in his right hand. The lohan wears an aubergine robe and is seated on a patterned mat with a spotted green border. He is placed against a patterned ground, sometimes referred to as a stone-wall pattern, painted in iron-red, green, yellow, and aubergine enamels, a most unusual design on porcelain decorated in polychrome enamels rather than underglaze blue.

The lohan on this dish may represent Kanaka Bharadvaja (Jp: Hatsura Tasha), whose attributes include the book and the fly whisk. By the Ming dynasty, the Chinese often depicted eighteen lohans (two more than the traditional sixteen imported from India), whereas the Japanese focused their worship on sixteen lohans. In Chinese Buddhist art, lohans are represented both collectively and as individuals, but in Japanese paintings and decorative arts, lohans are represented singly.[1]

The dish is covered with a glaze of bluish-green tinge; the glaze has pooled inside the foot at the long ends of the bottom. A bit of kiln grit adheres to the heavy and neatly beveled foot, while specks of green glaze dot the foot and the underside of the cavetto. On the bottom of the dish, a rectangular mark reading *da tang*, "great hall," is written in seal script in underglaze blue.

1. Baird, *Symbols of Japan*, p. 193.

101. Dish

五彩参禅布袋图菱形盘
Ming dynasty, ca. 1635–1645
Porcelain decorated in polychrome enamels
H. 3 cm; W. 18.5 cm
Butler Family Collection

This lozenge-shaped dish with a scalloped brown-glazed rim would have been one of a set of five or more dishes (Jp: *mukozuke*) made for the Japanese market. On this dish, Maitreya, the Buddha of the future, is depicted in the form of Budai (Jp: Hotei), the popular Buddhist god

of contentment. In this form, he is portrayed as a corpulent, bald-headed monk holding a rosary and wearing a beatific smile on his face.[1] A remote landscape is suggested by green and yellow-enameled rocks, lush iron-red grasses, and the promontory on which he sits and which drops off into seemingly endless space. Budai is sheltered by the proverbial pine with aubergine-glazed trunk, its branches partially obscured by iron-red clouds.

The dish is heavily potted and covered with a thick but glassy glaze of greyish tinge. The wide rectangular foot is carefully finished with three bevels. A *da tang*, "great hall," mark in seal script in underglaze blue within a double square is inscribed on the glazed bottom.

1. Weidner, *Latter Days of the Law*, pp. 192–93, no. 62. The Budai depicted on a plate in the *Fanshi mopu* [Fang's Ink Cake Manual] (1588) may have served as a model for the potter-painters of this dish. See Weidner, *Latter Days of the Law*, p. 407, no. 67.

102. Plate

青花五彩参禅布袋图圆盘
Ming dynasty, ca. 1630–1645
Porcelain decorated in underglaze cobalt blue
   and polychrome enamels
H. 2 cm; Diam. 21 cm
Butler Family Collection

The plate is painted in underglaze blue and iron-red, green, yellow, turquoise, aubergine, and blue enamels with the figure of Budai (Jp: Hotei), the Chinese popular god of happiness. He is considered another form of the bodhisattva Maitreya, Buddha of the future. Budai is depicted with bare midriff, baggy pants, and bare feet. He holds a leaf-shaped fan in his left hand; his right hand clutches a set of beads. His head, torso, sash, and feet are outlined in underglaze blue, and he is surrounded by two large *ruyi* clouds painted in underglaze blue with iron-red tendrils and two cranes with green and black-enameled wings and tails. He sits on an iron-red mat with an aubergine fringe. The plate's everted rim is decorated with twelve *ruyi* heads in underglaze blue alternating with iron-red *ruyi*, so that the plate represents a powerful wish for great happiness. In Japanese art, Budai is often depicted with a bag full of treasures; sometimes one or more male children are shown tumbling out of his sack.[1]

There is a 6.5 centimeter indentation in the center of the plate caused by the undercutting of the foot ring. The glaze is thick and has a slightly blue-green tinge; imperfections in the body have caused two large pinholes on the front. Small clumps of kiln grit adhere on opposite sides of the foot, which is unglazed and carelessly finished. The bottom is glazed and bears a mark reading *fu*, "happiness," within two blue squares.

1. Baird, *Symbols of Japan*, pp. 200–1.

103. Dish

青花白象纹花口盘

Ming dynasty, ca. 1625–1635
Porcelain decorated in underglaze cobalt blue
H. 5 cm; Diam. 19.2 cm
Private Collection

This footed dish with a flat scalloped rim is formed in the shape of a chrysanthemum. In the center of the dish, a white elephant with large round toes poses against a large garden rock. The rock ledge which supports the elephant appears suspended above a void. Long grasses sprout from either side of the rock, and two flowering branches

jut out above the grasses. Dragonflies swooping down on either side of the rock complete the composition.

Like many dishes made for the Japanese market, this one is rich in Buddhist imagery. The white elephant, sometimes depicted with six tusks, is the vehicle of the bodhisattva Samantabhadra (Ch: Puxian; Jp: Fugen), protector of the Lotus Sutra and those who study the Buddhist teachings. A brocaded mantle on the elephant's back holds a platform bearing a lotus pedestal topped with a lotus blossom, the Buddhist symbol of purity. A resplendent aura of light, symbolic of Buddhist law, springs from the lotus flower.[1] A very small rectangular box of the type used to hold a sutra or a relic sits in the

midst of the aura. The flowering branch to the right of the elephant is a tree peony, judging from its indented, three-pronged leaves.[2] Depictions of the peony, *fugui hua* or "flower of wealth and rank," implies wishes for high official rank and riches, a theme common to later Chinese porcelains. On the other side of the rock blooms the prunus, or plum blossom, which stands for purity and perseverance, two virtues revered by Buddhists. The five petals of the prunus signify the five blessings: good health, long life, a natural death, wealth, and a love of virtue.[3]

The body of this heavily-potted dish is composed of coarsely levigated clay. It was formed in a mold and rests on three short legs. Its greyish blue-green glaze is particularly thick and has pulled away from the back during firing, leaving short, unglazed striations in the furrows between the petals; the exposed body has fired a light orange. The rim above the cavetto is almost completely "moth-eaten," and the outer scalloped rim bears several *mushikui*.

1. Weidner, *Latter Days of the Law*, pp. 440, 414.
2. Krahl, "Plant Motifs of Chinese Porcelain," part 1, p. 56.
3. Bartholomew, "Botanical Motifs in Chinese Furniture," p. 45.

104. Dish

青花跻象图圆盘
Ming dynasty, ca. 1625–1630
Porcelain decorated in underglaze cobalt blue
Diam. 21.3 cm
Lent by the Asian Art Museum,
　　Gift of Roy Leventritt (B69P105L)

The form of this dish is ultimately related to Japanese stoneware dishes of the late sixteenth and early seventeenth centuries. It is very heavily potted and has a thick upturned rim decorated with a basket-weave border. Painted in the center is a boy riding a most curiously shaped elephant, which flourishes a lotus blossom in its raised trunk. The elephant's ear is shaped like an oak leaf, his tail like a long fly whisk, and his front feet like cat's paws. *Jixiang*, the act of mounting an elephant, is a homophone for the Chinese word meaning "auspicious," and so the propitious connotation of the image on the dish is generally secular. For many Chinese and Japanese, however, the iconography is also clearly Buddhist. The elephant is a vehicle of the bodhisattva Samantabhadra (Ch: Puxian; Jp: Fugen), protector of the Lotus Sutra and those who observe its teachings, and the lotus held aloft by the elephant's trunk is the Buddhist symbol of purity.

The cobalt pigment is rather black, and the potting characteristics are typical of early *kosometsuke* wares. The dish has warped slightly in firing, although not deliberately warped like an almost identical dish formerly in the collection of Richard Kilburn.[1] It has a grey, carelessly levigated clay body, and is covered with pinholes. The heavy glaze has a blue-grey tinge and has pulled away in one patch near the elephant's trunk. There are large bits of kiln grit and tool marks on the wide, rounded, and quickly beveled foot ring. Kiln grit also adheres to the front of the dish. A single blue line encircles the back of the dish just below the rim.

1. Kilburn, *Transitional Wares and Their Forerunners*, pp. 168–69, no. 134.

SELECTED CHINESE AND JAPANESE CHARACTERS

With the exception of proper nouns, the abbreviation (Jp) indicates Japanese terms or the Japanese equivalent of Chinese names and terms.

an, anchun	鹌，鹌鹑	Haoshui (Hao River)	濠水
araumi (Jp)	荒海	*hashigui* (Jp)	桥杙；桥杭
bagua	八卦	He Xiangu	何仙姑
bai guozhi	百果枝	*hehua*	荷花
bai guozi	百果子	*hou*	猴
bai lian	白鲢	Huangdi	黄帝
baizi	百子	Huizi	惠子
baoxiang hua	宝相花	Iga	伊贺
Bazhong huapu (Jp: *Hasshu gafu*)	八种画谱	*ikada* (Jp)	筏
Bifeng ti	碧峰题	*jiguanhua*	鸡冠花
binglie wen (Jp: *hyoretsumon*)	冰裂纹	*jinshi*	进士
Budai (Jp: Hotei)	布袋	*jixiang*	吉祥
Cai Yong	蔡邕	*jixiang*	跻象
Cao Cao	曹操	*juelu fenghou*	爵禄封侯
Caobenhua shipu	草本花诗谱	*juhua* (Jp: *kiku*)	菊花
(Jp: *Souhonka shifu*)		*junzi*	君子
chajin (Jp)	茶人	*kaiseki* (Jp)	怀石
Chan (Jp: Zen)	禅	*kan* (*kan* trigram)	坎
Chang'e	嫦娥	Kangxi	康熙
Chen Hongshou	陈洪绶	*kinrande* (Jp)	金襕手
Chenghua	成化	*kinuta* (Jp)	砧
Chongzhen	崇祯	*ko'akae* (Jp)	古赤绘
da ming nian zhi	大明年製	Kobori Enshū	小堀远州
da tang	大堂	*kōgō* (Jp)	香合
Damo (Jp: Daruma)	达摩	*kosometsuke* (Jp)	古染付
dian	点	Lan Caihe	蓝采和
Ding Yunpeng	丁云鹏	Lanting	兰亭
douji	斗鸡	Laozi	老子
ema (Jp)	绘马	*leiwen* (Jp: *raimon*)	雷纹
fangshi	方士	*li* (advantage, benefit)	利
feilong zai tian, huayuan yutao	飛龍在天，化猿于桃	*li* (*li* trigram)	离
		li (ritual)	礼
feng (Jp: *hachi*)	蜂	Li Tieguai (Jp: Tekkai)	李铁拐（铁拐）
Fenggan (Jp: Bukan)	丰干	*li yu*	鲤鱼
fu	福	*lianhua*	莲花
fugui hua	富贵花	*lianzi*	莲子
fukizumi (Jp)	吹墨	*lingzhi*	灵芝
Fukurokuju (Jp)	福禄寿	Liu Haichan (Jp: Gama Sennin)	刘海蟾（蝦蟇仙人）
Furuta Oribe	古田织部	Liu Ying	刘盈
guan	冠	Longhu Shan	龙虎山
gui yu	鳜鱼	Longquan	龙泉
guizi	贵子	*lu* (deer)	鹿
Han Gaozu	汉高祖	*lu* (emolument)	禄
Han Xiangzi	韩湘子	*lu* (heron; Jp: *sagi*)	鹭
Han Yu	韩愈	Lü Dongbin (Jp: Ryotohin)	吕洞宾
Hanshan (Jp: Kanzan)	寒山	*luohan* (Jp: *rakan*)	罗汉

SELECTED BIBLIOGRAPHY

Awakawa Yasuichi. *Zen Painting: Brushmarks of Infinity*. Tokyo: Kodansha International, 1970.

Baird, Merrily. *Symbols of Japan: Thematic Motifs in Art and Design*. New York: Rizzoli Publications, 2001.

Bartholomew, Terese Tse. "Botanical Motifs in Chinese Furniture." *Journal of the Classical Chinese Furniture Society* 2, no. 4 (Autumn 1992), pp. 36–50.

———. "Imperial Rebuses at the Qing Court." *Society of Asian Art Newsletter* 36, no. 1 (Fall, 1996), pp. 4–5.

———. *Myths and Rebuses in Chinese Art*. San Francisco: Asian Art Museum, 1988.

———. "One Hundred Children: From Boys at Play to Icons of Good Fortune." In *Children in Chinese Art*, edited by Ann Barrott Wicks, pp. 57–83. Honolulu: University of Hawaii Press, 2002.

Berkowitz, Alan J. *Patterns of Disengagement: The Practice and Portrayal of Reclusion in Early Medieval China*. Stanford: Stanford University Press, 2000.

Bickford, Maggie. *Ink Plum: the Making of a Chinese Scholar-Painting Genre*. Cambridge: Cambridge University Press, 1996.

Birrell, Anne. *Chinese Mythology: An Introduction*. Baltimore and London: Johns Hopkins University Press, 1993.

Brown, Kendall H. *The Politics of Reclusion: Painting and Power in Momoyama Japan*. Honolulu: University of Hawaii Press, 1997.

Butler, Michael, Julia B. Curtis, and Stephen Little. *Shunzhi Porcelains: Treasures of an Unknown Reign*. Alexandria, Virginia: Art Services International, 2002.

Butler, Michael, Margaret Medley, and Stephen Little. *Seventeenth-Century Porcelain from the Butler Family Collection*. Alexandria: Art Services International, 1990.

Butz, Herbert and Kawahara Masahiko, eds. *Chinesische Porzellane des 17. Jahrhunderts für Japan: Sammlung Georg Weishaupt*. Berlin: Museum für Ostasiatische Kunst, 1996.

Cahill, James. *Fantastics and Eccentrics in Chinese Painting*. New York: Asia House Gallery, Asia Society, 1967.

Cort, Louise Allison. *Shigaraki: Potters' Valley*. Tokyo, New York, and San Francisco: Kodansha International, 1979.

Curtis, Julia B. "17th and 18th-Century Chinese Export ware in Southeastern Virginia." *Transactions of the Oriental Ceramic Society* 53 (1988–89), pp. 47–53.

———. *Chinese Porcelains of the Seventeenth Century: Landscapes, Scholars' Motifs and Narratives*. New York: China Institute, 1995.

Eberhard, Wolfram. *A Dictionary of Chinese Symbols: Hidden Symbols in Chinese Life and Thought*. London and New York: Routledge and Kegan Paul, 1986.

Eskenazi, Ltd. *Two Rare Chinese Porcelain Fish Jars of the 14th and 16th Centuries: 7 November–30 November 2002*. London: Eskenazi, 2002.

Fong, Wen C. and James C. Y. Watt. *Possessing the Past: Treasures from the National Palace Museum, Taipei*. New York: Harry N. Abrams, 1996.

Fontein, Jan and Money L. Hickman. *Zen Painting and Calligraphy*. Boston: Museum of Fine Arts, 1970.

Fujioka Ryōichi. *Shino and Oribe Ceramics*. Translated and adapted by Samuel Crowell Morse. Tokyo, New York, and San Francisco: Kodansha International, 1984.

Fung Yu-lan. *A History of Chinese Philosophy*. 2 vols. Princeton: Princeton University Press, 1953.

Harrisson, Barbara. *Chinese Porcelain: the Transitional Period, 1620–1683, a Selection from the Michael Butler Collection.* Leeuwarden: Princessehof Museum, 1986.

Hayashiya Seizo. *Chanoyu: Japanese Tea Ceremony.* Adapted and translated by Emily J. Sano. New York: Japan House Gallery, Japan Society, 1979.

Hayashiya, Seizo and Henry Trubner. *Chinese Ceramics from Japanese Collections: T'ang through Ming Dynasties.* New York: Asia Society, 1977.

Hayashiya, Tatsusaburo, Masao Nakamura, and Seizo Hayashiya. *Japanese Arts and the Tea Ceremony.* Translated and adapted by Joseph P. Macadam. Heibonsha Survey of Japanese Art, 15. New York: Weatherhill, 1974.

Heinemann, Robert K. "This World and the Other Power: Contrasting Paths to Deliverance in Japan." In *The World of Buddhism: Buddhist Monks and Nuns in Society and Culture*, edited by Heinz Bechert and Richard Gombrich, pp. 212–30. London: Thames and Hudson, 1984.

Ho, Kwok Man and Joanne O'Brian. *The Eight Immortals of Daoism: Legends of Popular Daoism.* New York: Meridian Books, 1991.

Itō Toshiko. *Tsujigahana: The Flower of Japanese Textile Art.* Translated by Monica Bethe. Tokyo, New York, and San Francisco: Kodansha International, 1981.

Kakudo, Yoshiko. *The Effie B. Allison Collection: Kosometsuke and Other Chinese Blue-and-White Porcelains.* San Francisco: Asian Art Museum, 1982.

Katz, Paul R. *Images of the Immortal: The Cult of Lü Dongbin at the Palace of Eternal Joy.* Honolulu: University of Hawaii Press, 1999.

Kawahara Masahiko. *Ko-sometsuke.* 2 vols. Kyoto: Kyoto Shoin, 1977.

Kilburn, Richard. *Transitional Wares and Their Forerunners.* Hong Kong: Oriental Ceramic Society of Hong Kong, 1981.

Kotz, Suzanne, ed. *In Pursuit of the Dragon: Traditions and Transitions in Ming Ceramics, an Exhibition from the Idemitsu Museum of Art.* Seattle: Seattle Art Museum, 1988.

Krahl, Regina. *Chinese Ceramics in the Topkapi Saray Museum, Istanbul: A Complete Catalogue.* Vol. 2, *Yuan and Ming Dynasty Porcelains.* In collaboration with Nurdan Erbahar. Edited by John Ayers. London: Sotheby's Publications, 1986.

———. "Plant Motifs of Chinese Porcelain: Examples from the Topkapi Saray Identified through the *Bencao Gangmu*." Pts. 1 and 2. *Orientations* 18 (May 1987), pp. 52–65; (June 1987), pp. 24–37.

Kuroda Ryōji. *Shino.* Translated by Robert N. Huey. Famous Ceramics of Japan, 12. Tokyo, New York, and San Francisco: Kodansha International, 1984.

Kuroda Ryōji and Takeshi Murayama. *Classic Stoneware of Japan: Shino and Oribe.* Translated by Robert N. Huey (Shino) and Lynne E. Riggs (Oribe). Tokyo and New York: Kodansha International, 2002.

Lagerwey, John. *Taoist Ritual in Chinese Society and History.* New York: Macmillan, 1987.

Liao Ping, ed. *The Yongle Palace Murals.* Beijing: Foreign Languages Press, 1985.

Little, Stephen. "Ko-sometsuke in the Asian Art Museum of San Francisco," *Orientations* 13 (April 1982), pp. 12–23.

———. *Taoism and the Arts of China.* With Shawn Eichman. Chicago: Art Institute of Chicago, 2000.

Masuo, Shin'ichirō. "Daoism in Japan." In *The Daoist Handbook*, edited by Livia Kohn, pp. 821–38. Leiden: Brill, 2000.

Murase, Miyeko, ed. *Turning Point: Oribe and the Arts of Sixteenth-Century Japan.* New York: Metropolitan Museum of Art, 2003.

Nishida, Hiroko. "Collecting Chinese Ceramics in Japan." In "The History of Collecting Oriental Ceramics in East and West," *Vormen uit Vuur* 191/192 (2005/2), pp. 29–37.

Ong, Hean-Tatt. *Chinese Animal Symbolisms.* Petaling Jaya, Selangor Darul Ehsan, Malaysia: Pelanduk Publications, 1993.

Rinaldi, Maura. "Dating Kraak Porcelain." In "Kraak begeerlijk porcelain uit China," *Vormen uit Vuur* 180/181 (2003/1–2), pp. 30–41.

———. *Kraak Porcelain: A Moment in the History of Trade*. London: Bamboo Publishing, 1989.

S. Marchant and Son. *Exhibition of Ming Blue and White Porcelains: the Drs. A. M. Sengers Collection*. London: Marchant and Son.

Sen, Sōshitsu XV, ed. *Chanoyu: the Urasenke Tradition of Tea*. Translated by Alfred Birnbaum. New York and Tokyo: Weatherhill, 1988.

Sheaf, Colin and Richard Kilburn. *The Hatcher Porcelain Cargoes: the Complete Record*. Oxford: Phaidon / Christies's, 1988.

Stinchecum, Amanda Meyer. *Kosode: 16th–19th Century Textiles from the Noruma Collection*. New York: Japan Society and Kodansha International, 1984.

Tanaka, Sen'ō and Sendÿ Tanaka. *The Tea Ceremony*. Rev. ed. Tokyo, New York; London, Kodansha International, 2000.

Valder, Peter. *The Garden Plants of China*. Portland, Oregon: Timber Press, 1999.

Varley, Paul. *Japanese Culture*. Honolulu: University of Hawaii Press, 2000.

Wang Qingzheng. *Qinghua youlihong* [Underglaze Blue and Red]. Shanghai: Shanghai Museum; Hong Kong: Woods Publishing Company, 1987.

Watson, Burton, trans. *The Complete Works of Chuang Tzu*. New York: Columbia University Press, 1968.

Werner, E. T. Chalmers. *Myths and Legends of China*. New York: Brentano's, 1922.

Williams, C. A. S. *Outlines of Chinese Symbolism and Art Motives*. 3rd rev. ed. New York: Dover Publications, 1976.

CHINA INSTITUTE GALLERY EXHIBITIONS: 1966–2005

** 1. SELECTIONS OF CHINESE ART FROM PRIVATE
COLLECTIONS IN THE METROPOLITAN AREA
November 15, 1966–February 15, 1967
Curator: Mrs. Gilbert Katz

** 2. ART STYLES OF ANCIENT SHANG
April 5–June 11, 1967
Curator: Jean Young

** 3. ANIMALS AND BIRDS IN CHINESE ART
October 25, 1967–January 28, 1968
Curator: Fong Chow

** 4. GARDENS IN CHINESE ART
March 21–May 26, 1968
Curator: Wan-go H.C. Weng

** 5. CHINESE JADE THROUGH THE CENTURIES
October 24, 1968–January 26, 1969
Curator: Joan M. Hartman

** 6. FOREIGNERS IN ANCIENT CHINESE ART
March 27–May 25, 1969
Curator: Ezekiel Schloss

** 7. CHINESE PAINTED ENAMELS
October 23, 1969–February 1, 1970
Curator: J.A. Lloyd Hyde

**8. ALBUM LEAVES FROM THE SUNG AND
YUAN DYNASTIES
March 26–May 30, 1970
Curator: C.C. Wang

** 9. MING PORCELAINS: A RETROSPECTIVE
October 29, 1970–January 31, 1971
Curator: Suzanne G. Valenstein

**10. CHINESE SILK TAPESTRY: K'O-SSU
March 24–May 27, 1971
Curator: Jean Mailey

** 11. EARLY CHINESE GOLD AND SILVER
October 21, 1971–January 30, 1972
Curator: Dr. Paul Singer

** 12. DRAGONS IN CHINESE ART
March 23–May 28, 1972
Curator: Hugo Munsterberg

** 13. WINTRY FORESTS, OLD TREES: SOME
LANDSCAPE THEMES IN CHINESE PAINTING
October 26, 1972–January 28, 1973
Curator: Richard Barnhart

** 14. CERAMICS IN THE LIAO DYNASTY:
NORTH AND SOUTH OF THE GREAT WALL
March 15–May 28, 1973
Curator: Yutaka Mino

** 15. CHINA TRADE PORCELAIN:
A STUDY IN DOUBLE REFLECTIONS
October 25, 1973–January 27, 1974
Curator: Claire le Corbeiller

** 16. TANTRIC BUDDHIST ART
March 14–May 24, 1974
Curator: Eleanor Olson

** 17. FRIENDS OF WEN CHENG-MING:
A VIEW FROM THE CRAWFORD COLLECTION
October 24, 1974–January 26, 1975
Curators: Marc F. Wilson and Kwan S. Wong

** 18. ANCIENT CHINESE JADES FROM THE
BUFFALO MUSEUM OF SCIENCE
April 3–June 15, 1975
Curator: Joan M. Hartman

** 19. ART OF THE SIX DYNASTIES:
CENTURIES OF CHANGE AND INNOVATION
October 29, 1975–February 1, 1976
Curator: Annette L. Juliano

** 20. CHINA'S INFLUENCE ON AMERICAN
CULTURE IN THE 18TH AND 19TH CENTURIES
April 8 –June 13, 1976
Curators: Henry Trubner and William Jay Rathburn
(Exhibition traveled to the Seattle Art Museum,
October 7–November 28, 1976.)

21. CHINESE FOLK ART IN AMERICAN
COLLECTIONS: EARLY 15TH THROUGH
20TH CENTURIES
October 27, 1976–January 30, 1977
Curator: Tseng Yu-Ho Ecke

** 22. EARLY CHINESE MINIATURES
March 16–May 29, 1977
Curator: Dr. Paul Singer

** 23. I-HSING WARE
October 28, 1977–January 29, 1978
Curator: Terese Tse Bartholomew
(Exhibition traveled to the Nelson Gallery of Art,
Kansas City, February 19–May 21, 1978,
and the Asian Art Museum of San Francisco,
June 16–September 21, 1978.)

**24. EMBROIDERY OF IMPERIAL CHINA
March 17–May 28, 1978
Curator: Jean Mailey

** 25. ORIGINS OF CHINESE CERAMICS
October 25, 1978–January 28, 1979
Curator: Clarence F. Shangraw

** 26. ART OF THE HAN
March 14–May 27, 1979
Curator: Ezekiel Schloss

27. TREASURES FROM THE METROPOLITAN
MUSEUM OF ART
October 25–November 25, 1979
Curator: Clarence F. Shangraw

** 28. CHINESE ART FROM THE NEWARK MUSEUM
March 19–May 25, 1980
Curators: Valrae Reynolds and Yen Fen Pei

29. CHINESE PORCELAINS IN
EUROPEAN MOUNTS
October 22, 1980–January 25, 1981
Curator: Sir Francis Watson

* 30. FREEDOM OF CLAY AND BRUSH THROUGH
SEVEN CENTURIES IN NORTHERN CHINA:
TZ'U-CHOU TYPE WARES 960–1600 A.D.
March 16–May 24, 1981
Curator: Yutaka Mino
(Exhibition originated at Indianapolis Museum of Art.)

**31. THE ART OF CHINESE KNOTTING
July 29–September 21, 1981
Curator: Hsia-Sheng Chen

**32. MASTERPIECES OF SUNG AND YUAN
DYNASTY CALLIGRAPHY FROM THE
JOHN M. CRAWFORD JR. COLLECTION
October 21, 1981–January 31, 1982
Curator: Kwan S. Wong, assisted by Stephen Addiss
(Exhibition traveled to the Spencer Museum,
University of Kansas, March 14–April 18, 1982.)

33. THE COMMUNION OF SCHOLARS:
CHINESE ART AT YALE
March 20–May 30, 1982
Curator: Mary Gardner Neill
(Exhibition traveled to the Museum of Fine Arts,
Houston, June 22–August 22, 1982, and the Yale Art
Gallery, New Haven, October 5, 1982–April 17, 1983.)

* 34. CHINA FROM WITHIN
November 4–December 12, 1982
A Smithsonian Institution Travelling Services
Exhibition, organized by the International Photography
Society in cooperation with the China Exhibition
Agency, Beijing, and the Chinese Embassy,
Washington, DC

**35. BAMBOO CARVING OF CHINA
March 18–May 29, 1983
Curators: Wang Shixiang and Wan-go H.C. Weng
(Exhibition traveled to The Nelson-Atkins Museum of
Art, Kansas City, July 24–September 11, 1983, and
the Asian Art Museum of San Francisco, October 3,
1983–January 15, 1984.)

36. CHINESE CERAMICS OF THE
TRANSITIONAL PERIOD: 1620–1683
October 21, 1983–January 29, 1984
Curator: Stephen Little
(Exhibition traveled to the Kimbell Art Museum,
Fort Worth, May 26–August 26, 1984.)

* 37. MASTERPIECES OF CHINESE EXPORT
PORCELAIN AND RELATED DECORATIVE
ARTS FROM THE MOTTAHEDEH COLLECTION
February 10–March 7, 1984
U.S.–China 200 Bicentennial Exhibition,
organized by Anita Christy

**38. CHINESE TRADITIONAL ARCHITECTURE
April 6–June 10, 1984
Curator: Nancy Shatzman Steinhardt
(A permanent travelling exhibition of China Institute.
Shown at Allegheny College, Meadeville, PA,
March 28–April 19, 1985; Marlboro College,
Marlboro, VT, September 11–October 31, 1985;
State University of New York, Binghamton,
January 7–February 27, 1986.)

** 39. CHINESE RARE BOOKS IN
AMERICAN COLLECTIONS
October 20, 1984–January 29, 1985
Curator: Soren Edgren

40. THE SUMPTUOUS BASKET: CHINESE
LACQUER WITH BASKETRY PANELS
March 20– June 3, 1985
Curator: James C.Y. Watt

** 41. KERNELS OF ENERGY, BONES OF EARTH:
THE ROCK IN CHINESE ART
October 26, 1985–January 26, 1986
Curator: John Hay

* 42. PUPPETRY OF CHINA
April 19–June 29, 1986
Curator: Roberta Helmer Stalberg
Organized by the Center for Puppetry Arts, Atlanta

43. SELECTIONS OF CHINESE ART FROM
PRIVATE COLLECTIONS
October 18, 1986–January 4, 1987
Exhibition celebrating the 60th Anniversary of China
Institute and the 20th Anniversary of China Institute
Gallery, organized by James C.Y. Watt and
Annette L. Juliano.

* 44. 1987 NEW YEAR EXHIBITION

* 45. CHINESE FOLK ART
April 4–May 30, 1987
Curator: Nancy Zeng Berliner

** 46. RICHLY WOVEN TRADITIONS:
COSTUMES OF THE MIAO OF
SOUTHWEST CHINA AND BEYOND
October 22, 1987–January 4, 1988
Curator: Theresa Reilly

* 47. 1988 NEW YEAR EXHIBITION
February 4–February 24, 1988

** 48. RITUAL AND POWER:
JADES OF ANCIENT CHINA
April 23–June 19, 1988
Curator: Elizabeth Childs-Johnson

* 49. STORIES FROM CHINA'S PAST
September 17–November 12, 1988
Curator: The Chinese Culture Center of San Francisco

For information on availability of these titles and others, please contact China Institute in America at (212) 744–8181

* No catalogue or exhibition catalogue published by another institution

** Catalogue out of print

Ta Chun Hsu
Virginia A. Kamsky
Yue-Sai Kan
William W. Karatz
Angela H. King
James J. and Helen D. Lally
John Jody and Yue Tao Lee
John M. Leger and Sophie Orloff
Karen Li
William M. Lipton
William E. and Helen Y. Little
Robert W. and Virginia Riggs Lyons
Warren A. Mackey
Clare Tweedy McMorris and Howard McMorris, III
Robert E. and Joyce H. Mims
Mechlin and Valery Moore
Veronica Ogden
William Raiford
Theresa M. Reilly
James and Joanne Quan Reynolds
Diane H. Schafer and Jeffrey Stein
Peter Scheinman and Barbara Giordano
Linda Rosenfield Shulsky
David Solo
Anthony M. Solomon
Martha Sutherland
Charles J. Tanenbaum
Patricia P. Tang
Theow-Huang Tow
Shao F. and Cheryl L. Wang
Laura B. Whitman and Thomas Danziger
Savio and Emily Chang Woo
Denis C. and Kathleen Yang
Laurie and David Y. Ying
Robert P. and Barbara Youngman

Academic
Annette L. Juliano and Joseph L. Geneve
Mrs. Henry H. Weldon

GALLERY COMMITTEE

Yvonne L.C. Wong, *Chair*

Susan L. Beningson
Claudia Brown
John R. Curtis, Jr.
Robert Harrist
Maxwell K. Hearn
Annette Juliano
David Ake Sensabaugh
Jerome Silbergeld
Marie-Hélène Weill
I. Peter Wolff

GALLERY

Willow Weilan Hai Chang, Director
Pao Yu Cheng, Manager of Art Education (DCTA)
Jennifer Choiniere, Gallery Registrar

DOCENTS

Peggy Hung, Senior Docent
Stephanie Lin, Senior Docent
Roberta Nitka, Senior Docent
Dong Shin Chang
Larry Chang
Viviane Chen
Pamela Frances Yap

VOLUNTEERS

Mary McFadden
Jeannette N. Rider
Anna-Rose Tykulsker
Jackie Handel
Ann Dillon
Hunter Demos

Photo Credits

China Institute

80 Years of Expertise
1926 ~ 2006